I Live with Birds

Roy Ivor with his favourite pine siskin

HANCE ROY IVOR

I Live with Birds

FOLLETT PUBLISHING COMPANY
Chicago   New York

Publisher's Note
The Ryerson Press wishes to thank Angus McLellan
and Barry Penhale for their counsel and editorial aid in
this publishing project.

598.25
foor
c. 4

T-4030

FOLLETT PUBLISHING COMPANY

1010 West Washington Boulevard
Chicago, Illinois 60607

Foreword

If you were to search the world you would find very few truly unique personalities, but Roy Ivor would be among them. Born at Strathroy, Ontario, in 1880, he went west with his parents two years later. Here he grew up on a section of farm land a few miles south of Moose Jaw, Saskatchewan, amidst the teeming prairie wildlife of that time. When ten years old he discovered the first nest and eggs ever found of the Richardson's merlin, or western pigeon hawk.

When Roy was seventeen the family moved to Toronto and he became engaged in earning a living. But during his most active years, following the death of his father, he turned his back on the normal compensations of city life and retreated to a secluded area, near Erindale, some twenty miles west of Toronto. In 1928 he built a cottage in the shadow of the woodlands and overlooking an acre of assorted weeds which he cultivated to attract our native seed-eating birds. Here he lived with his mother until she passed on, aged one hundred and five.

Originally his property comprised forty acres, but it eventually became reduced to include only the immediate three-acre sanctuary surrounding his home. And he proved to be no recluse, for soon people of every station in life—business tycoons, politicians, college professors, school children and just ordinary folk seeking relief from the routine of life—found him out. Many visitors came from far places. I remember talking to him when a car from the United States drove up his laneway. The lady had driven five hundred miles to bring him a bluebird which she had found in her garden as a fledgling. It had become a total pet. But since it was unlawful to keep in captivity any native wild migratory insectivorous bird, she was ordered to release it. However, before an officer arrived to seize the bluebird she was on her way with it to Mr. Ivor's Erindale sanctuary. He of course had federal and provincial permits for the keeping of native birds.

Soon after Mr. Ivor had become established in his new surroundings he found himself virtually living with birds and studying their behaviour, a field which, until that time, had been left almost untouched. Possibly his approach has not always been in accordance with scientific notions, and the fact that he has worked largely alone leaves him without the backing of any scientific group. It is also true that his work may have been more sentimental than coldly objective, and he has been variously criticized for his generally soft-hearted approach. But a new generation is now with us that sees only his achievements, which are all that count.

Indeed anyone less sentimental could hardly have accumulated his wide fund of knowledge on bird behaviour. I had saved several published articles on the hearing range of song birds and had taken them to show to Mr. Ivor. They were the result of findings in the department of ornithology at Cornell University. Their substance was that a songbird could not hear the human voice because it was pitched in too low a key. It was said that only very high notes, such as the shrill calling of baby birds, could be heard by their parents.

"When you talk to your canary, he may be listening as he watches your lips move, but he doesn't hear a word you say," wrote Dr. Arthur A. Allen, then head of the university's department of ornithology. "When I talk to my pet crow in a low voice it is little wonder he turns a deaf ear to my crooning," Dr. Allen continued. He then explained that, as proved by tests made in Cornell's laboratory of ornithology, a ruffed grouse could "drum with impunity, even at night in woods inhabited by horned owls because the vibration frequency of the grouse's drum was only about forty cycles a second and the horned owl could hear only to seventy cycles."

To me these were extremely interesting facts; I felt that I had added to my knowledge. After I had finished expounding this new discovery in the field of scientific investigation, Mr. Ivor spoke: "It has been proved that the bluebird down there in the garden cannot hear my voice, but how do you account for what you are going to see?"

The bird was seventy-five or one hundred feet away. Mr. Ivor took a mealworm from one of his cultures and said, "Joey, come and see what I have for you!" Like a flash Joey came streaking to him. Mr. Ivor kept his hand closed around the worm and when Joey could not find it he flew to one of the cultures, looked down at the burlap covering and then up to Mr. Ivor. Of course Joey got his worm and away he went. Then Mr. Ivor in his usual normal voice, called various other birds by name and they all responded individually. It seemed to me to be a practical demonstration of how inconclusive scientific findings can be. Nowhere else in the world could such a demonstration of behavioral response have been observed.

Of course these birds were all Mr. Ivor's pets. "But," as he remarks, "tame birds will show you hundreds of facets of their behaviour which are not generally known. Wild birds don't trust you, neither do they provide you with much of a clue as to why they act in a certain way."

Since moving to Erindale he has, each summer, cared for some two hundred and fifty young and injured birds which have been brought to him. Many of these have been migrants, travelling at night, that crashed into picture windows, television towers, lighthouses and tall lighted buildings. But his real reason for going to Erindale was to study the behaviour of birds, for he was certain they possessed far more personality than was generally believed. In order to get behind their normal barrier of fear he had to hand-rear them. His first step was to obtain permits from both the federal and the provincial wildlife departments.

Inevitably he began having visitors. Strangers would stand astonished as apparently wild birds would fly down out of the trees and alight on his shoulder. On one occasion he had gone a quarter-mile from his cottage through his winding wooded lane to the highway to pick up his mail. Just as the mail carrier arrived a rose-breasted grosbeak alighted on Mr. Ivor's shoulder and began tugging at his ear. The mailman had never before seen such a colourful bird and he stood watching in amazement. "He is just ringing the dinner bell," Mr. Ivor responded, "he knows I have peanuts or sunflower seeds in my pocket."

It is this kind of close relationship that has enabled him to accomplish his work with birds. Today, as the result of articles on bird behaviour in various publications, including several in *The National Geographic Magazine*, he is known throughout North America and in Great Britain; recently he was quoted in a new book published in Russia.

One of Mr. Ivor's special studies has been the habit, indeed the frenzy, of many kinds of birds to "ant." In this operation the bird seizes an ant in its beak, then goes into unusual postures or contortions as it rubs the ant over various areas of its feathers. A photograph of a blue jay in the process of anting, taken in Mr. Ivor's sanctuary and published, January 1943, in *The Auk*, journal of the American Ornithologists' Union, was said to be the first photograph ever obtained of a bird anting. Later, in an article in *The Illustrated London News*,

Dr. Maurice Burton said: "Roy Ivor, a Canadian naturalist, has made a more extensive study of this extraordinary behaviour in birds than anyone else."

Mr. Ivor is as close to birds and they to him as it is possible to get. In the evening when he sits down to relax a goldfinch invariably goes to sleep on top of his glasses. I remember a female bluebird named Josie that would never go to bed until Mr. Ivor "tucked her in" for the night. During the first six months of her life Josie was a cripple and he had to wait on her constantly. Even after she had gained full use of her faculties she demanded to be petted and stroked. The seasons passed and Josie had five young in her nest when she was killed and eaten by a sharp-shinned hawk.

But that didn't turn Mr. Ivor against hawks, for at the present time he has a big female red-tailed hawk that fusses over him as if he were her own nestling. But she is a savage and powerful aggressor toward anybody else. Consequently he is forced to keep her in a large flight cage. Last summer this big hawk raised a red-shouldered hawk that was brought to Mr. Ivor as a downy youngster.

There is always something unusual occurring around his three acres. In April he visited a nesting box attached to a tree at the edge of his neighbour's woodlot. So that it would be acceptable to a fastidious tenant he removed the lid of the box and scooped out what he took to be refuse, tossing it to the ground. Three weeks later a visitor to the sanctuary, curious as to the material found in the bird box, pulled the bundle apart, and six eggs of the white-breasted nuthatch were found buried deep in rabbit's fur.

Apparently the nuthatch, which usually nests fairly early in the spring, protects its eggs from the cold by covering them well until the full complement are laid and the bird is ready to incubate. In a regretful mood for having destroyed the nest, Mr. Ivor again lifted the lid of the box. To his surprise the nuthatch was sitting on six more eggs and she refused to be budged.

One of his many observations concerns the male rose-breasted grosbeak. The spring plumage of this colourful songster, after it has reached its third year, is black and white and its breast is vividly rosy. But in August, when it moults, the black parts of this bird turn a rusty colour and its rosy breast fades.

Now if the bird were to lose some of his feathers, and new ones immediately grew in, one might think that the replacements would be the same colour. But they are not. In the case of the rose-breasted grosbeak, if a black feather is lost in early spring it is replaced by one belonging to autumn. If in turn this autumn feather is lost, regardless of the time of year, it is replaced by a black one belonging to spring, or the breeding season. This indicates that when the bird was but a single cell within the egg all the plumages of its lifetime, arranged in the order of requirement, were there, too.

We are told by the experts that most of the parent-nestling relationship is instinctive. Parents come with food and pop it into the mouth that is open the widest and held the highest. So the strong survive and the weakling just naturally starves to death. But Mr. Ivor has been a watcher at hundreds of nests where he has had the total confidence of the parent birds. He denies absolutely that birds are nothing more than a bundle of instincts and reflex actions. There is, he claims, individuality in every parent bird and it is rather remarkable how different individuals of the same species can be. Over the years he has had much satisfaction demonstrating the errors of professional ornithologists whose experiences have been with wild birds. He says birds are like people, you must become acquainted with them in order to know them, especially their confidential ways. And these ways are never demonstrated by wild birds because of the element of fear. All we see of them is the wild side of their behaviour.

Mr. Ivor has made extensive studies of the capacities of birds, such as their special senses. When a Harvard professor published the statement that "there is no experimental evidence whatsoever of anything remotely resembling reasoning power in birds," Mr. Ivor invited him to his sanctuary where he would receive first-hand proof that he was wrong.

When I first knew Mr. Ivor there were six blue jays around his home, living as wild birds. But each was an affectionate, entertaining pet. When he called they responded to their individual names, and he never tired of describing the personalities which distinguished them as individuals. Blue jays, he claimed, were among the gentlest and most intelligent of birds. Always they try to avoid trouble. A pair will stay together during their lifetime and remain in the same district.

Though I myself prefer to observe wild creatures under wild conditions, I am also ready to admit that you cannot really know a wild animal until you have lived with it and enjoyed its personality and its confidence.

HUGH M. HALLIDAY

Some Canadian baby birds: brown thrasher, three blue jays, bluebird, brown thrasher

Preface
Why a Songbird Observatory?

Eighteen youngsters with wide-open bills clamoured for food every minute from dawn to dark. There should have been fourteen parents to take care of these little fellows. To feed them and their brothers and sisters would have kept all their mothers and fathers busy from sunup to sundown, but I had taken the place of their parents. It was just one round all day long of making up nestling food and filling those always-waiting baby mouths. I could never seem to still the anticipating, quivering wings and coaxing calls. It was "me too, me too" all the time. "Bonnie" Bluebird, the lost Bonnie, was with them and that wonderful foster mother, Vee the wood thrush, and—but first I must tell you "why." Then you may wonder why Little Blue divided his treats between his mate and me; why bluebird Josie chose my half-closed hand for her sleeping place; and why I came to realize the lovableness of baby birds.

Perhaps when you read of them, and so many others, you will realize what enjoyment there has been for me as I studied the habits and emotions of so many of our trustful native birds; that while I spent long hours with them as my companions down through the years I added to "the knowledge of the ages."

Fascinating as are all native birds, particularly songbirds, pleasurable as is their companionship, this is our only excuse for keeping them: to add to our knowledge and pass such knowledge on to others. Even the gaining of this knowledge must be by permission of federal and provincial authorities, for under international regulations our native birds are protected and such permission is given, not that we may keep them as pets, not for our pleasure, but only for study.

Such study I have carried on for almost forty years, living parts of each day with various species of native songbirds in their large summer or winter quarters: quarters where they may fly and exercise back and forth over a distance of more than a hundred feet. Rather more than a cage, it is a songbird observatory—is it not? The idea of such an observatory did not come to me suddenly. Perhaps it came to me unconsciously early in the morning of a far-off day nearly seventy-six years ago when the buckskin pony was hitched to the two-wheel cart, and two boys of ten and twelve drove south. Ten miles—and dusky wings hovered and dived in a bewildering pattern over the Big Slough as hundreds of black terns arose from the beds of reeds, their querulous cries protesting our presence so near their nests. With juvenile thoughtlessness and ruthless desire my brother Hugh and I stripped; and gathered eggs, and ducked under the water to alleviate the burning rays of the summer sun; gathered and ducked and gathered until we had over a hundred, mostly black tern and "mudhen."

Alone on the farm in the shack that night we tossed and turned, and in the morning to relieve the dreadful pain of sunburn, each, in the ignorance of childhood, poured turpentine over the red. Today I can still see those two-inch strips of skin we peeled in ribbons from our shoulders and backs. Perhaps those strips of vanished skin alone saved us from the licking we deserved for our wholesale robbing of nests, for when we arrived at our home in Moose Jaw, a tiny town in what was then Assiniboia, in the heart of that great prairie that is the Canadian West, we were told in emphatic terms that only one egg from a nest must ever again be taken for our collection.

Often I have wondered if there was not born in those days of the long-ago the interest and love of birds that has persisted for the greater part of my life. That interest probably was intensified later by the knowledge that we had been the first to find the nest and eggs of the western pigeon hawk or Richardson's merlin,* as it was then called. As the years passed I developed a distaste for collecting eggs and gradually acquired a love for the birds themselves. But it was many years before I learned that there were great gaps in our knowledge of their lives, of the facts of bird behaviour and personality; and I began to feel that there was one way only of filling many of these gaps. That was to obtain and maintain a bird's confidence to such an extent that it would show its true personality. The bird in the wild rarely shows this even to the most careful and patient observer.

Thus when I saw a young blue jay on the ground, out of its nest a day too soon, unable to fly and in danger from a straying cat, I picked it up. Carrying it to the house, I put it in a cage and placed this inside my bedroom window. Its parents found the little jay there and fed it

*See Walter Raine's *Bird-Nesting in Northwest Canada* (Quebec: Hunter, Rose and Company, 1892).

through the bars of the cage. From outside they looked on while I too fed it. Then, suddenly, they left all the feeding to me although I often saw them where they could watch. They were feeding other nestlings within sight of their eldest and I wondered why they were so unconcerned. Also I wondered if established confidence would eventually throw some light on their actions. So I decided to keep the young bird.

This little fellow proved so interesting; showed me so many of the ways of a blue jay that I did not know before, that it came to me that much, hitherto unknown, could be learned of our native birds if I could live in intimate contact with them: have them trust me as a human friend of ours will trust us. Thus the songbird observatory evolved, and here, throughout the years, I have been able to learn of the entrancing and perplexing ways of many hundreds of birds of many species. In time I learned that my thought as I picked up the little jay—that to know a bird we must live with it just as we must live with a human really to know him—was justified.

Near Erindale, Ontario, my three acres of woodland, marginal growth and meadow—established as a songbird sanctuary nearly forty years ago—are situated at the end of a lane that meanders for a quarter of a mile through a heavily wooded ravine. Surrounding the sanctuary are some thirty acres of woods composed of many varieties of native deciduous trees and shrubs with a scattering of hemlocks and pines. The woods, adjoining an apple orchard, make the location ideal.

Here at Windinglane Cottage it has been my privilege to carry on an intimate study with mostly hand-reared birds as subjects; birds such as bluebirds Joey and Josie, Little Blue and Bonnie, and a host of others just as lovable, just as interesting—and just as informative. Their confidence—in many cases their complete trust—has, I feel, allowed me to delve deeper into their characters and, possibly, has gained for me a truer perspective of their lives than would have been possible by any other means of study.

Perhaps in no way can I make clearer my purpose in studying birds which, through absence of fear of man, reveal characteristics generally hidden, than by quoting Alexander Skutch, who has written: "For myself, each year I incline more strongly to put confidence in those rare flashes of sympathetic understanding that seem to penetrate the outer husk of a bird and reveal the life within; I believe they are more likely to disclose the truth than those laborious analyses of behaviour by which we attempt to discredit them. If I must incur the risk of error I prefer to incur it with the gateways of the spirit open rather than shut."

Orphan birds are brought to the house, placed in a cosy, relined robin's nest, kept warm and well fed, and when they have attained independence—have learned to feed themselves—they are placed in the winter observatory. This home, facing south, is forty-four feet long (fourteen of this length being a storeroom), ten feet wide, and eight feet high. Almost the entire south wall is made up of windows with removable double sashes. In the spring these windows are taken out and the birds have access to a flight cage of almost the same size as the observatory.

Almost all the upper part of the north wall is occupied by a large wall cage with removable partitions. By partitioning, fourteen large cages are made available for birds that may have to be separated from others for a time in the spring when considerable fighting takes place. Spring is mating time and fierce jealousies arise. Fighting over mates can be very serious; the ones who get too pugnacious must be separated from the others. When not thus in use, the cages form part of the observatory. This observatory, joined to my cottage at one end, is heated in winter by oil, and a fairly constant temperature between fifty and sixty degrees is maintained.

Here about one hundred birds belonging to twenty-five or more species have their winter home. In size they range from the tiny indigo bunting to the large blue jay. Usually they are almost equally divided between what we call, loosely, seed-eaters and insectivorous birds.

The summer observatory, joined to the winter observatory by a half-inch-mesh wire flyway, is located some sixty feet to the south-east; it is octagonal in shape, twenty-five feet in diameter and ten feet high in the centre. Eight large breeding compartments are arranged about the centre flight, which is reserved for unmated birds. In each compartment is a small gate that may be opened to allow the nesting bird to seek food outside the observatory. Arbor vitae and spruce form most of the planted shrubbery used for roosting and nesting sites.

Birds that pair have liberty while rearing young. Some birds, such as blue jays, have as much as eight months of daytime liberty each year.

You may ask with reason, as some do, "How is it possible for you, not being callous, to take tiny nestlings from their parents as you sometimes do?" Often I ask myself that same question. Each time I take a nestling I have to remind myself that science may be served and, if I take the bird, it may live a comfortable life for years; while if left to nature's care, its life may be for a day, a week or a month. (The average life of all the smaller birds probably is less than a year and a half.)

Countless millions of young birds in the wild never live to leave the nest. Countless millions more never live through the fledgling stage. Nevertheless, even with my interest in gaining knowledge, sometimes I only look—and creep away.

Yet, also, many nestlings that have fallen from their nests, young birds whose nests have been destroyed by storm, are brought to me to care for and rear. Some of these are kept for study and others are released when able to care for themselves.

The ones I keep become well loved and lovable companions, representatives of the millions of their kin, the keepers of the field, the orchard and the forest. How lovable, you shall see when you come to know the bluebird, Little Blue, as he comes from the trees when I call; or wood thrushes, Vor and Vee, from a woodland path to accept some tidbit from my hand, then off to their home in the songbird observatory where ever-hungry nestlings are waiting.

Are they and their companions happy, if we may use such words to describe emotions in birds? Has the songbird observatory become home to them as our home is to us? You will wonder, as I do, why Vee adopted fifteen little birds of several different species and reared them to independence; why a bluebird, Bonnie II, gives back to me a favourite morsel of food I give to him; why Deedee the chickadee played a cute trick on me. The "why" is ever present as we puzzle over the ways of birds, but in this volume I shall touch just lightly on the why. Rather, I shall introduce to you some of the ones who have made my studies possible.

The lives of our songbirds are sufficiently interesting, even dramatic enough, to be described in a truthful manner. In no instance have I drawn upon imagination, except in one illustration—a friend's walk in a pasture field where he found the nestling home of the first Josie, and which he pictured to me in part. All else I shall describe has come under my own observation. For the splendid photographs reproduced in this book I am especially indebted to Hugh M. Halliday and Bernard Corby.

Windinglane Cottage, Erindale, Ontario   H. ROY IVOR
November 6, 1967

Contents

Contents

Illustrations

Illustrations

Roy Ivor with Rajah the golden eagle

Rajah, the Wounded King

"It's a glorious day! Let us go out and kill something! Particularly, let us go out and shoot anything that flies. It matters not that what we shoot is of value to our neighbour. It matters not that it has a right to life, even as you and I. Nor does the terrific suffering of a wounded creature need to affect us. What do we care?" Of course, these words are not audible. They are only in the hearts of the unthinking, the callous and those with the blood lust in their veins. But soon one of the winged ones will pay.

It was mid-October—the eastern-pointing shadows marked the time for milking. A farmer, rounding up his scattered herd, saw a large dark object near a distant cow. As he approached, to his surprise a great bird arose, took wing and flew a near two hundred yards to alight in tumbled exhaustion. The farmer ran to seize it before it could fly again, enclosed it in his arms and carried it home. So many would have clubbed this noble bird, wounded and ill: unable to protect himself. Laudable on the farmer's part, was it not? Later, I wondered. A neighbour called; told me of the great hawk in the farmer's yard; asked me to go with him and tell him what it was.

A hawk indeed! A magnificent golden eagle is standing on one foot in a dirty, abandoned chicken-house. His body droops, but his proud head is erect, his piercing brown eyes defiant. On the floor a dead pigeon lies, killed by the farmer and thrown before the eagle that he might eat. Poor fellow, how can he eat, with one leg so badly crippled by shot that he cannot set his foot upon the floor, let alone use his great talons to hold the bird. He is weak from hunger, loss of blood and a deadly creeping infection.

He seems bewildered, afraid of us; tries to hide where there is no place to hide. The great hooked beak and long curved swords of

1

talons look dangerous, yet it is necessary that he be examined. It must be determined how serious his hurt, for it must be great indeed to bring that powerful body to such a pass as this. I borrow a glove for one hand so that a possible attack may be warded off, an attack which could have serious consequences if it comes. As I quietly approach him, he does not try to get away, nor does he make a move that indicates attack. I feel his wounded leg and find that it is badly swollen. I stretch his wings and see that there is no serious injury there. A few of the great primaries have been shot off, but nature will readily take care of these in time. No injury to the body can be seen; no blood or broken feathers on his breast.

All the while the great brown eyes watch every move I make, but every move is slow and gentle, for, he believes he is in the presence of his worst, and possibly only, enemy—man. I want him to know, if he can know, that no harm can come to him from me. Now, as this is written in the long afterwards, I think he knew.

I secure a knife and cut the pigeon into pieces and offer a piece to him. He refuses it but eyes it greedily. "Perhaps," I think, "he does not like the feathers." These I pluck from a piece, and then how greedily he takes it from my fingers! Soon all of the pigeon is down that capacious throat. A drink of water is then offered, which he refuses.

Again I try to examine the wounded leg. I cannot examine it well, for I am still a little afraid of those powerful talons and that great curved beak. Now that he has been fed, he may not prove so docile. Again he watches every movement I make, but offers no resistance. I suggest that I have him taken at once to an animal hospital in the city, as his life probably is in great danger. Now I begin to wonder about the altruism of this farmer. He demurs. I wonder if there is a greedy gleam in the farmer's eye. Then I know there is. At least five dollars' worth of gleam.

A telephone call to a city naturalist—he and a game warden are on the way. It is now night, but the need is great. The wounded eagle is seized from the protesting farmer and taken without more delay to the clinic. The bird-loving doctor examines the injured leg through the fluoroscope, finds a badly shattered joint, the wound full of maggots and gangrene so rapidly advancing that a few more hours' delay and the great brown eyes would close to open no more.

Now science is at work. The wound is cleaned, the maggots removed and two heavy injections of antigangrene serum given. This doctor, working late at night, gives all he knows, and it is enough. For what? The reward of money? No. For his love of birds. The verdict? "He will recover. No charge."

2

Rajah on his shelf

This great injured bird is brought to me. I place him in a small enclosed compartment of the birds' summer home. Here a large heavy roost is set up, and on the floor is sacking so that he may rest at night. Next morning I place him on the roost, which undoubtedly he prefers. Several times a day I wash and bathe his injured leg with salty water and keep the wound open to allow for proper drainage. Later, bandages with soothing ointment are bound around the leg. (This latter treatment was, I am afraid, not quite in accordance with the instructions given by the doctor. I did not quite understand the reason then, but he did not want the wound to heal too quickly—wanted drainage for a while.)

At first, Rajah—for so I have named this gallant bird—gazes suspiciously at the long narrow bandage. He stretches his neck, looks down at my hands as I begin to wind the bandage around the injured joint—the shot had entered and gone through the joint between the tarsus and the tibia—the knee joint to us. I watch his eyes—eyes that are now as soft and brown as those of a deer. No fierce glare is there, so I know it is safe to finish the winding.

Usually he leaves the bandage on; but sometimes, when I visit him in the morning, I find the yard-long wrapping neatly laid upon the roost. He has carefully unwound it, for there is not a mark or tear upon the cloth. Several times a day I exercise his foot so that circulation will not stop; so that his toes will not become stiff and useless, for he cannot put his foot upon the roost. Does this regal and supposedly fierce king of the air object to all this "fussing"? Not a bit! He seems to understand. Every movement on my part is closely watched. Unavoidably, I cause him some pain, pain so great that at times his whole big body trembles. But not once does he offer to use that great hooked beak in retaliation for the pain I cannot help but inflict. Food is taken from my fingers so gently that never a nip is given. Surely he must know.

The little room is much too small for such a large bird, and he gazes longingly through the window. For a time I must keep him where he is while I plan. Two-inch-mesh wire strung tight on posts, would give Rajah at least the semblance of freedom. I make the enclosure very large so that, if he desires, he can exercise a little those great wings. Then a large platform is built in one corner, covered with sacking and a deep layer of straw. A perch is erected at the other end, some thirty feet away, for him to rest upon if he wishes during the day. Using heavy gauntlets I carry him to his new home.

For him to be carried goes much against his will. That is the one indignity I place upon him, and one which he resents. He does not attempt to bite or fight, but he does struggle so to get out of the tightly

4

clasped arms. Somehow one cannot help but feel the humiliation placed upon this great bird by carrying him. But "must is must" sometimes.

Rajah is far happier in his new quarters. At once he adopts the straw-strewn shelf as home, and how clean he keeps it! A lesser bird would foul his roosting place and his bed would have to be renewed often. During fine days, all through the daylight hours, he stands upon the perch.

Days pass, but each day shows no apparent improvement in the wounded leg. Weeks pass and, after the third, I take him to the clinic to be X-rayed. During the twenty-mile journey I hold him on my lap and he makes no untoward move. But once, as the car swerves around a corner, his balance is upset and, to save himself, the great talons of his injured foot contract and one talon penetrates deep. He did not mean to hurt me.

The X-ray shows that the bone is knitting; that one tendon has been severed; that there are several pieces of lead between the tendons. The severed tendon! That is bad, for if it ever joins it will take a year to heal.

After three long months he still must stand on the uninjured foot. He becomes so tired. His big body is heavy, and after several hours upon the perch he trembles. Perhaps, though, this trembling is from the intense pain of the injured leg. I know it is, at times; for after he gets off the perch and hops on one foot over the long stretch of ground to his roosting shelf, or to the water pan in which he soaks his feet for long periods, his sore leg trembles violently, for he must touch it to the ground as he hops along.

Otherwise, he seems quite well. His big body is plump and round, but why not? A whole rabbit once a day for six days (at least one day a week he must go without: that is nature's way) is skinned and cut up for him, and he eats it, bone and all. His dish must be held by me so that he will not have to stoop. It hurts him too much to reach down so far as the floor of his roost. The dish is held until the last little scrap, just beneath my thumb, is gently taken. Is the thumb in danger? Not once. There is no treachery there.

He seems to be quite satisfied with his temporary home. Not once has he attempted to beat upon the enclosing wire. Even the door of his compartment may be left open. It might as well not be there for all he seems to care. Not a sign of viciousness does he show. Not that he likes any liberties to be taken now. He is too proud for that. The time has come when I must not stroke his golden head or touch the feathers of his back. Should I now attempt such liberties there seems to burn such fierceness in those brown eyes that I withhold my hand. I know that most of the tiny, trustful songbirds resent a touch upon their feathers. So much more might Rajah resent this touch. But I have stroked his head in earlier days and I want to do so now. I place my finger lightly against his breast. The feathers of his crown become suddenly erect—a sure danger signal. I desist, for I have seen the lightning stroke, almost too swift to see, with which he grasps the newly killed squirrel I place before him. I remain near and quiet. The crest smooths down and his gaze turns from me to some distant scene. Then I see such piercing eyes as I have never seen before in man or animal. I move and his stare returns to me. Now again the mellow, trustful expression has reappeared. I move closer; keep my hands behind my back; stand close beside him. Slowly he bends that magnificent head and pulls at a button on my coat.

The wounded leg is badly swollen still; his pain intense, as one can tell. Three months of this excruciating torture—and how much more? Just because one of us indulges his weasel-like desire to kill.

More months have passed, and during their passing Rajah has gained sufficient strength in his wounded leg to be able to reach down to his dish and take from it the cut-up food. No more shall I have to hold the food dish before him so that he may eat. Each day more pressure seems to be put upon the crippled foot, and soon a rabbit or squirrel is put before him whole and partly skinned. He jumps upon it, driving the great talons of the uninjured foot into the fur with amazing speed. Then, up goes the proud head; the feathers on the crown arise, and a glare comes into the wonderful eyes. The rabbit is his. Who will dare take it away!

In early spring the slow moult of the eagles begins; just the odd feather dropped from the wings. More natural food—wild food, not tame rabbits—must now be secured so that the great, strong feathers may grow to take him, in the coming time, to the heights. Now tender young groundhogs are laid at his feet and he strengthens. Slowly, though, does nature give back strength to the leg and the foot and the claws.

Summer passes, the moult seems over, the foot appears fully healed. Great wings spread in perfect symmetry, strong and ready. A great company of naturalists arrive to see him go. The whole side of the cage is taken down. But—we wait in vain. Not a move toward liberty does he make. Freedom is now his for the taking. Why his reluctance to leave?

For days I wait. Rajah does not want to go, nor do I want him to go; but I feel it is best. I know his leg is strong again. I know his place is in the air—beyond all other birds perhaps. How can I persuade him to go? There are only two things he is afraid of: my gauntlets and a stick. His fear of the first is because I always use gauntlets in handling him. And gauntlets mean imprisonment in my arms. Imprisonment which he resents with all his great strength. I think his fear of a stick is that he must associate it with a gun. There can be no other reason.

It is now November again, almost a year to the day. I try to coax him out of the wide-open cage by throwing a rabbit on the ground. Not a move will he make. I hunt for a stick in the woods, go into his great cage. That semblance of a gun is too much for him. Rajah takes to the air. Across the ravine to an oak he flies and rests there a while, then comes back and alights on the top of the cage. Again I show him the stick—and send him again to the man with a gun? Do I miss him? Yes. Shall I see him again?

Should I have given him his liberty? Often, I wonder. Often, I wish I had not. The years have passed. Rajah has never returned.

Robins in White

They were as white as newly fallen snow—Papeek, Weewee and Cherilée.

The true full albino—pink eyes, yellow bill and legs—is one of nature's rarities, but these three were not rare only. They were one of nature's wonders. So far as it has been possible to learn there is no other record of three albino songbirds, and a partial albino, in one nest; and what's more, the nest of normally coloured parents.

An almost unbelievable message came to me one day in June: "Can you come to Meadowvale at once? There are three white young in one of our robins' nests, getting ready to leave. Now there is one on the ground. Hurry!" I hurried. Some years before I had had a white robin. She was with me for quite a number of years. Always I hoped for a mate for her: watched closely each robin nest and at times even day-dreamed of finding a nest of white young, but it was no more than a dream, for there is that assumed natural law which says "No." So I could not believe my good fortune until I arrived and actually saw them.

All four nestlings had sailed from the nest far up in the eaves and had been gathered into a cage. Not only did I want to experiment with the Mendelian laws, but it was doing them a kindness to tame them, for, because of the poor eyesight of albinos, their lives in the wild would be short. Not only might their days be much lengthened, but, if I took them, I might add to our knowledge of birds. I had no thought at the time of the task I would have or the future trouble they would give. Perhaps if I had—but no, I think I would have taken them anyway, for the partial albino and the three full ones would, in the future, furnish a remarkable and exceptional opportunity for study. Much as I wanted to take advantage of this rare chance for advancing knowledge, I found

The last day on which the albino robins accepted food from the food-stick

it necessary to allow for parental feelings. The parents were frantic, but I knew that one young one left with them would quiet their fears, so the partial albino was given back to the father and mother.

After being safely brought to their future home they would be, like all nestlings, starving of course. Well, if they were they did not admit it. Of all the stubborn youngsters with which I have dealt these were surely the worst. No gaping yellow mouth greeted me when I offered them food. Instead, the food-stick had to be forced between resolutely shut beaks, each mouthful a struggle. Every half hour for one whole long day, the three fought the food-stick. Then two learned what it meant, gave in to the lure of delicious food, and gaped when I called. Not the third. He did not like me, or the food-stick, or the food. For four full days he held out, then—suddenly accepted the inevitable.

Soon the food-stick had no more attraction. Gradually it had come to them that the food jar was there always while the food-stick was not. The strenuous days were over—for me. Not for them however: robin pugnacity had not been eliminated along with the colour. Yet with all their contending, perhaps as yet it was only youthful play.

It was the middle of summer when the one banded red, called Papeek, first developed the true robin temper. For so young a bird that was remarkably soon, and was an indication of what was in store

9

for the future. Not only his brother and sister, but any bird near was attacked while he fed. The food in the food cups belonged to him only and he was quite willing to prove it. As they grew older, the temper of robins unfolded in each, and strife was almost continual. Not only did each attempt to master the other, but they continued to attack other birds without fear or favour—except Little Blue and Josie the younger. These two bluebirds were "not having any" from even so large a bird as a robin.

When Papeek, the eldest, was sixty-four days old he began to warble in a juvenile way. Then shortly Cherilée too showed that he had a voice; so it appeared likely that two of the three were male birds. This was most gratifying, for usually, they say, albinos are females.

Although pugnacity was now a dominant trait, not all was in earnest, for often they played. At times Papeek would pick up an object such as a leaf, hold it up before Weewee or Cherilée as though daring each to take it away while he or she crouched nearby with head held low to the ground. Then an erratic chase would begin that was as likely as not to develop into a quarrel. At times I would see one or the other dodging and gyrating behind an arbor vitae in exuberant gambols all by itself, which reminded me so much of a kitten chasing its tail.

All three undoubtedly were precocious, for not only did they become viciously combative while young, but in early September Weewee began picking up grass and placing it in a cedar with the intention of building a nest. Never before do I remember a bird of the year trying to build.

In the middle of winter it was necessary to put Weewee in prison for she was endangering the lives of all birds. She came close to killing the evening grosbeak, old Beauty, in one swift attack. Then before spring both Papeek and Cherilée, more vicious than ever, had to be caged.

Early in spring I let Weewee out of her cage. She must have a chance to choose her own mate. It would seem to be Papeek whom she chose, for often she clung to the bars of his cage. Although she wanted to build, I could not let her do so until she and her mate were moved to their summer home. There were too many curious eyes —and bills—in the winter home for her to be a successful mother there. Too—that temper of hers: not another bird would be safe.

The long, cold, wet spring, the move to a home unknown, so upset what should have been the even tenor of their lives that, although I supplied them with all they could need, all thoughts of nesting were

10

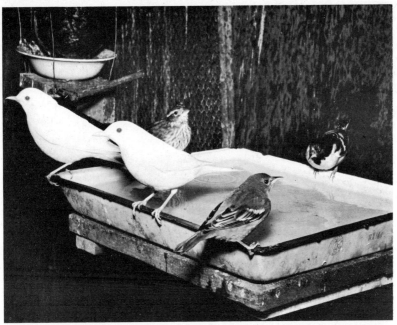

Albino robins Papeek (left), Weewee (centre); female rose-breasted grosbeak Sherree (behind Weewee); juvenile Baltimore oriole (right front); Ori, male Baltimore oriole (background)

lost. Cherilée mated with old Robbie and twice she attempted a nesting; but a chipmunk had other ideas, and each time she lost all her eggs.

Another winter came and again it was prison for Weewee. Bobo, the male bobolink, and a little white-throated sparrow paid with their lives by not being careful near her. Papeek and Cherilée were never through fighting, but they were so evenly matched and so alert to each other that no damage came. An unfortunate thing this vicious behaviour, for they were a very beautiful three. Still white as snow, and like statues at times as they stood facing each other, they were almost unbelievable birds. Unbelievable too, as I looked at them often at dark while, close together, they roosted as though the best friends in the world.

For nearly nine years they were with me and never outgrew their bad tempers. Only once in all that time did they again attempt to nest, and oddly enough Weewee chose her brother Papeek for her mate. She built the typical robin nest, laid four eggs, and in due time the little ones hatched. And—she ate each one as it emerged from the shell. Always we have so much to learn. I should have fed her a diet much higher in animal protein. Had I done so I might still have white robins.

They Too Were So Blue

Dick and Pet; Uno and Lady! These were blue jays all: mates for life. And there was Babe—a blue jay of a different stamp. Of the faithful four there is much to tell. But first, let me tell you about Babe.

Babe was the youngest in the nest—Dick and Pet's nest. Perhaps I should not have interfered. Sometimes I wonder if birds know when a nestling has come into the world too late or too weak. It seems that nature in some mysterious way imparts that knowledge to the parents, for at times we find a nestling in the nest after the others have gone: neglected, uncared for—and still. It seems to be nature's way of making certain that only the strong survive.

I could see Pet searching in the thorn tree part-way down the ravine. A bright flash of blue nearby revealed Dick. In their hunting they never seemed to be far apart. I waited beside their nest admiring the beauty of the four nestlings. I held my finger just above their heads and spoke a word to them. Three little bills opened wide, three little heads reached up, for they knew me well. One did not raise its head, and I wondered. Then the mother was beside the nest. The nestlings responded to her soft, throaty "bizz" and the heads reached twice as high. A little lower than the others, the youngest now too reached up. First one and then the other and the third received an equal share—the youngest, not a bite. Then Dick came to the nest with a full bill. He gave Pet part, then both divided it among the three only. The smallest one appeared almost as well as the others: somewhat smaller, certainly. But why had they left it out? Surely, I thought, the next visits would be different and the baby would be fed. I waited there.

In a few minutes, Dick and Pet were back and again all their food was divided among the oldest three. I knew now it had not been an oversight. They were purposely neglecting the youngest bird.

I hastily made up nestling food and did that youngster eat! It was insatiably hungry and I thought I should never be able to fill it. The parents did not object: I could take care of it if I wished. They took advantage of the nestling food I brought, cramming the three little throats with this easily secured substitute for the caterpillars they had been hunting. I visited the nest often that day but not once did I see the youngest being given any attention. They ignored it as though it had never hatched—as though it had never existed.

Thinking that it would be stronger in the morning I left the neglected bird with its parents in the faint hope that they might see the error of their ways and take pity on it. It was not to be. If this baby jay was to have a chance at life it would have to come from me. Gently I removed it from the nest. That seemed quite satisfactory to the father and mother. Both stood on the rim of the nest as I lifted the youngster out—they did not turn a feather. A discarded robin's nest, freshly lined with grass was ready: a discarded home for a discarded nestling.

Wild blue jay and nestlings

13

She had been a poorly feathered bird. Good food and regular meals soon changed her into a seemingly strong fledgling. The stubby tail with its wide blue bands and narrow black began to lengthen. The coming crest was now a ridge across the bold and handsome head and it was time to leave the nest. Unaccountably she lingered there. I wondered why but had too much on my mind to be other than vaguely troubled.

The reason for this strange attachment to the nest became painfully apparent. She knew her name very well and she knew my hands as parents, security, protection. One day I called to her—"Babe"—and held out my hands. She answered eagerly, hopped from the nest and tumbled to the floor. I called her again. She attempted to rise but only fluttered on her side. I picked her up. As I placed her on the palm of my hand I saw two tight little fists. The toes of both her feet were curled up. I straightened them out but they would not stay. Gently I spread out one wing. It seemed stiff. She looked up at me and greeted me with a hoarse, gurgling note unlike her usual greeting. As I put her back in her nest she turned her head to watch me—the only part of her body she could move. Lovely, brilliant, blue—and paralyzed.

I knew now that she was as helpless as when I first saw her in the nest. Her parents must have sensed that this baby was defective and, in their way, showed kindness in discarding her. In my way, though, I was still determined that Babe should flourish. I changed her food, sought veterinary advice, pored over texts on paralysis and even pestered my medical friends. I was certainly not encouraged, for paralysis is rarely cured in man or bird. Week after week and month after month I tried every palliative either suggested to me or self-conceived. One day I came up behind her and, to my delight, she freely turned her head and looked back at me. Gradually, the tight muscles relaxed and she could move her tail: then she could reach over her wing to preen her feathers. The improvement was almost imperceptible though. The daily change could not be seen: it was as slow to be noticed as the change in a growing plant.

She still tumbled to the floor when I called her out of the nest. She was still unable to rise and her feet were still tightly curled. I would pick up the little bundle of blue feathers and she would cuddle in my hand, content.

A new home for Babe was lined with cotton batting. It was a wire cage with an open top. She was taught to eat and drink from little cups. When she tumbled on her side in her new home, I often let her try to get up without assistance. In the soft batting lining she could exercise the stiff muscles and she soon learned to rise. In time, I was

14

able to let her out on the floor where she could hop about the room, but her feet soon became sore with hard callouses which formed on the curled-up toes. This was another worry—and a new challenge.

After much thought, I secured some quarter-inch-thick sponge rubber and fashioned from it a pair of sandals. Three deep slots were cut in the front of each and one in the back. I stretched out the toes of one foot, placing each toe in the proper slot, and sewed the rubber together above. Then I sewed on the other sandal and put her on the floor. She tumbled onto her side. Time after time I had to place her on her feet until, at last, she was able to balance on her great clumsy shoes. Awkwardly at first, and with much practice and persistence, she learned to hop about the room and rarely fell. When she did fall she would struggle for a time and then call, in a peculiarly frightened manner. I always knew when she was in trouble. Of course, I did not let her out of the cage unless I was near enough to hear the cry.

Blue jays, among the most intelligent of birds, become perhaps the most trustful of all when reared by hand. They endear themselves to us to an extent that would not be thought possible to anyone who knows them only as among the shyest and most cautious birds of our woodlands—viewed strictly as wild birds.

Babe had all the fascinating characteristics of her kind but, being a cripple with a continuing need for care, she became part of our personal lives. She was never content unless sitting on my lap. She would sit there by the hour if I let her. Sometimes, when I was busy, I could not take her up and she would become comically offended. Hopping into the darkest corner of the room, under the couch, she would sulk. I would call her and coax her, but she would not come out. Then I would have to reach under, pick her up and place her in my lap. All her sulkiness vanished in a moment.

Summer came and her open-topped cage was often placed on the back veranda. Sometimes Dick and Pet, Lady and Uno, with their young would come to visit her. When they entered her cage for some tidbit they saw there, Babe screamed in panic for she did not know them. They were strangers. She was helpless and she knew it. Her screams were screams of fear and, perhaps, for me. When I came running and stretched down my hands for her, the screams ebbed to coaxing, gurgling notes and she would flutter her crippled wings as she begged me to take her up. Once in my hand, she felt so safe that she could look directly at Lady and her crowd. Still softly gurgling, she would burrow deep against me and seemed to ask that I take her away.

I would take her to the living room so she could hop around the

15

floor until she got over her fright. Where Babe was concerned that would not do at all. Tappety-tap-tap, the little padded feet (the rubber soles had hardened and each hop made a distinct tap as she crossed the hardwood floor) made directly for me wherever I sat. When she reached my feet she crouched, then attempted to fly on useless wings to my knee. I always picked her up, stroked the beautiful head, stretched, a little, the drooping wings and let her tie even tighter that incomprehensible bond that exists between man and the animals who adopt him.

Weeks passed, months passed and winter came. Uno and Lady, Dick and Pet could not frighten her now for Babe saw them and the white outdoors only through the windows. Only in my lap, or in my hands, could she see out even then. She was not much interested in what she saw. Babe would rather play with my fingers or have me stroke her blue head and back. Although I have mentioned a slight improvement in Babe's condition, she was still completely dependent on me.

One day in spring I cut the threads that bound her feet; pulled off the rubber sandals and put her on the floor. She hopped! The toes were as straight and flexible as nature intended them to be. The callouses had long gone and I finally had hope for the future of this little jay because this was the first concrete evidence that paralysis was retreating.

Summer came and Babe's progress continued. A little more spread to her tail; a little more height to the lift of her wings; fewer tumbles as she hopped about the room. She was allowed to bathe more often for she rarely fell on her side in the bathing dish now. Yet, not for an instant must she be left alone in the bath.

Birds love to bathe and Babe was no exception. How she loved to soak herself in the shallow pan! The pan had to be shallow for she could not right herself quickly enough should an accident happen. Only half an inch of water was safe and I had to stay with her until she was ready to get out—my hand ever ready to right the dripping blue jay if she happened to overbalance. It was like bathing a baby.

Baby, incidentally, was the only reference we made to her for many months—a means of easy identification because she had been the youngest in Dick and Pet's nest. It was automatically shortened to "Babe" somewhere along the line. Her mother's name, "Pet," derived from an expression always used when she was referred to as a young bird—"that bird is a real pet."

The summer went well and Babe's health improved, interminably slowly as it seemed. One day, early in her second autumn, I placed her

16

Baby blue jay about fifteen days old

bathing dish on the front porch. Babe eagerly hopped in and, at that
moment, someone called me. I was away only a couple of minutes
but she had fallen.

As quick as that, the long, patient struggle to help this bird toward
normal life had ended. All I felt, at the time, was that I had merely
prolonged a life that was not meant to be. Looking at it realistically,
it is likely that Babe would never have gained a normal bird's freedom.
On the other hand, I did prove that it is possible, with care and attention, at least to improve a paralytic condition hitherto considered
untreatable. The only drawback is the real loss felt when a pet bird
is gone.

   Dick and Pet visited Babe's outdoor nest but she had gone. And of
Babe, there is no more to tell.

The Foursome

Pet was a year younger than Dick. These two were mates for many years. Dick, as a young bird, had been very shy. He had learned his fear before he came to me, and remained shy and easily frightened for two whole years. After his fear left, however, he became bold and domineering with me: so unafraid that he did not hesitate to give my finger a good rap if I denied him what he wanted, or appeared to take too much for granted. When still quite young, the muscle of a snail which he was feeding on, got caught around his tongue. To free him from the snail I had to cut the muscle, which meant that Dick's bill must be opened wide. His bill had not hardened to the adult stage and I probably held it open a little bit too wide. It never closed tightly again and this was an advantage to him when he decided I needed a lesson. The gap in the bill was barely perceptible but, when he struck my hand with it, the slightly opened bill really hurt—he merely wanted to show me that it was not good policy to deny him anything he wanted.

Lady and Dick were sister and brother. Lady was gentle, and became to us—"Ladybird"—shortened to "Lady" as she became an adult. She carried the name all her life—and it fitted her. Lady seemed to have little use for Dick. Although they never quarrelled, their personalities were very different. Dick never did like to be petted, even when shyness left him. Lady could not get enough of it. Ordinarily, a bird will give what we know as affection only to its mate and young, although this appears to be no more than seasonal. Most of us can become very fond of a pet but rarely is that fondness returned in kind. Lady returned the affection, particularly as roosting time drew near.

Blue Jays retire quite early as it is unsafe for them to roost outside the

18

observatory. I always called them in from the trees when dusk approached. Each evening after I called them home, Lady would fly to my arm and climb up underneath my chin where she would proceed to settle for the night. Often I stayed for long minutes, sometimes till nearly dark, reluctant to disturb her. It seemed to me that this was more than confidence. Even after Lady took a mate she did not lose this endearing habit. It might have been that she was not overly attached to her mate, Uno, as she might have been if she had chosen a wild jay for herself. When she did accept Uno, she was faithful to him throughout the rest of her life. But she gave him many bad moments before making her decision. Uno courted Lady and, although she accepted food from him at times, she took it casually. She showed no real sign of interest in him. Spring was passing and I wondered why Lady was so apathetic. Uno, to me, was the acme of all that a male jay should be. He would come to my shoulder and prance there while he sang his low, sweet and varied jay song so close to my ear.

In the observatory there was a large, thick thorn tree: a perfect nesting site. Thorn twigs were scattered liberally on the ground for use as nesting material. Uno posed before Lady, showed off his beautiful plumage, attempted to give Lady food, then flew off to search for suitable twigs. He would carry them to her, enthusiastically. At last, half-heartedly, she accepted his attentions and gave in to his persistence. She chose a site, listlessly took the twigs he brought to her and arranged them to form a nest. It grew so slowly that it was obvious her heart was not in it.

Before the nest was half-completed, a visitor arrived. He had a moving-picture camera and saw an opportunity to record the fact that these birds were not prisoners but were given liberty at times. We felt that, as the nest was only half-finished, Lady would not abandon it but would return as soon as she was called. We let her out to pose among the trees. It was odd that we should have chosen that very moment—because a wild blue jay appeared. I called to her often —"Lady, Lady"—but she never answered.

Uno? He was distraught! No other word seems to fit. He called to her almost incessantly: for nearly five long days. He would go to the half-finished nest and crouch down in it. Sometimes he carried a twig. For the most part, though, he gazed toward the trees.

On the fifth day of Uno's loneliness, a neighbour, walking down the winding lane called to me, "Here is your Ladybird." Lady was coming home. But she was bringing a wild mate back with her!

My desire to have her back was so strong, and Uno's distress so great, that I allowed my superior human judgment to be swayed.

Dick and Lady as youngsters

I decided she would come back and thereby also decided the course events were to take. I called, "Lady," and she swooped to my shoulder and rode into the observatory. Uno seemed beside himself. He danced and pirouetted, flew to the nest, picked up twigs and sang in an excess of happiness. And Lady? I can still hear her, after these many years, frantically calling to her mate: still see the violent flight against the enclosing wire. With open, panting bill she exhausted herself in her efforts to join the wild mate she had chosen. I would not make that kind of decision again. Only a bird? Perhaps. But within that little body was a capacity for suffering I can only liken unto our own.

20

Her wild mate called from the hawthorn with entreating, enticing notes. His shimmering blue wings hovered for a moment over her prison, he flew swiftly off toward their chosen home. Exultant calls changed in midair to what seemed like pleading as his wing beats slowed and he circled to return to the hawthorn. Again and again he entreated. All day long she answered and clung to the wire. Day after day he called and she tried to join him. Finally, he came back less often—and then no more.

During this time Uno tried to feed her and interest her in their nest. He even tried to build the nest himself but she did not care. She could not forget her wild choice, or forgive me for separating them. She would not play with me and ignored me when evening came.

It took a long time but she finally got over it. When another summer came Uno and Lady were inseparable—but sometimes I wondered about her total acceptance of the observatory. Often, when the birds were being called home, before the approach of evening had cast long shadows on the ground, they came swiftly to me—all but Lady.

I listen! I hear her calling and know she is alone. Again and again I call. Dusk is on its way and there is always danger in the treetops then. The marauding little screech owl is waking from his daytime sleep. Lady heeds my voice at last. Winging swiftly through the trees she flies to my shoulder and greets me with soft, endearing notes.

Uno showed his desire for Lady's company throughout the winter, but did not display to her until spring was well on its way. Now she accepted his advances and in due time the nest was built and her first egg laid. The small gate in her compartment was opened, as well as the gate in Dick and Pet's, and the four were given their daytime liberty. The gate was still closed at night but, when the eggs were hatched, the entrance was never closed. Food had to be sought for the nestlings as soon as the dawn broke and it was too early for me. When the young were able to take care of themselves, the parents and the flighted young who wished to come were called to the observatory and shut in for the night. In the fall they were closed in until wild jay migration had been completed. They were given daytime liberty once again until the northern migration of hawks began about the first of April.

I always looked forward to calling them in at night. They were called by name and responded readily—all but Pet, and I will tell you about her shortly. A name must be short for a bird really to learn it and, usually, used constantly from the time the bird is very young. Can you imagine calling them in to the observatory at night—"*Cyanocitta cristata*"? If they did come to their technical name, and I doubt that

21

they would, they'd all come at once. Ornithologists who deplore the habit of naming pet birds, will never have the thrill of watching them respond to their individual names.

Pet knew her name as well as did the others. She knew quite well, too, that she was being called to her roost. Each evening all four came flying out of the woods but only three flew to me. Pet flew to a shrub or corner post and stayed there. She was just as tame as her three companions but I often wondered if this was a display of pure stubbornness. Ever since she had been a young bird she would come to me only when she was good and ready. She was quite willing to go to roost inside—when it suited her.

I stood just outside the observatory one evening as Dick, Uno and Lady came in. Pet was in one of her stubborn moods and although I called until exasperated she would not come in. I threw her favourite food, raw peanuts, through the door thinking she would go in after them. She merely fluffed her feathers and watched while Dick picked them up. I was in a hurry that evening and extremely out of patience with her. Dick was on my wrist and, unconsciously, I looked at him and said "Dick, call Pet." To my astonishment Dick called her and she answered him at once and flew in. From that time on, when she refused to go in when I called her, I told Dick to bring her in. It seems incredible, I know, and I have no explanation for it; but my problem was solved. It was easy to understand Pet's responding to Dick's call, but for Dick to understand a command seems inconceivable. I suppose I could have started some research along this line but I was much too busy at the time to attempt a new project. I was an observer, not a trainer, and I did not try to prove that Dick truly understood certain statements. It did happen, however. Not once—but over and over again.

Lady had never lost her confidence in me even though it was late in the second summer after I had separated her from her chosen mate before she regained her former extraordinary attachment.

I am certain that Lady considered (if birds do consider) the observatory her home and the surrounding woods the special territory of herself and Uno, in company with Dick and Pet. Certainly she took it for granted that the wild shrubbery between the observatory and the house, as well as all it contained, belonged to her. This was proved to me conclusively when I was picking caterpillars from a witch-hazel shrub. I had several of these worms in my hand and was just reaching for another when she saw me trespassing. Like a blue dart she alighted on my wrist and hammered at my fingers. These caterpillars belonged to her and she meant me to know it. She did not want them. Birds are

Dick and Lady—half grown

not very fond of insects that feed on witch-hazel leaves; but, as I reached for another caterpillar, she snatched the worm herself. I offered the rest to her. She refused them and flew to my shoulder where she shrilled at me. After teaching me a lesson, she flew off.

Summer passed and it was time for the birds to lose their liberty again. Late one autumn afternoon I noticed a flock of sixteen blue jays nearby. I thought little about it until it was time to call the foursome in. Dick, Pet and Uno arrived—but no Lady. She had gone again.

One year later, on the eighth of August, Dick and Pet were gathering food for their nearly grown young (they were late to brood that year) and Uno was in the observatory. Suddenly, from a treetop a blue jay swooped and alighted on my hand. Her soft, gurgling notes of affection greeted me and when she hopped to my finger and rode there, I knew it was Lady. Uno made a great fuss. It was long past the mating season but you could not tell from his actions; nor from hers. It was almost a year since she had left us, yet the memory of her home, her mate and of me had not diminished at all. Dick and Pet, not ordinarily demonstrative, came to greet her and showed mild excitement.

Lady never left again. She and Uno, Dick and Pet lived on with me year after year, raising their broods and going about their business in the manner of all blue jays. I recorded my observations of them until they were no longer able to answer my call. That was long ago; but I still remember them as some of the most lovable and interesting birds ever to live in the observatory. Especially when the nights are cool and the leaves are beginning to turn in autumn—when the birds come in at night.

Elves in Feathers

Because of his confiding ways, our tiny black-capped chickadee is known so well to most that little I could tell about him would be new. We who study birds, however, will throughout the years make friends of one or two of these elves who will become personalities because of some outstanding characteristic which sets one apart from all his fellows. In all my years of fellowship with them—and there can be fellowship, for they are with us all the year—only three have shown such trust, such endearing qualities, that they have remained in memory beyond the rest.

It was many years ago (in fact that same winter I first met Yak, the white-breasted nuthatch, and Yak-yak, his mate), that I came to know so well the first of these. I had my hand upon the window sill, placing sunflower seed there, when a little fellow came flying from the trees and without the slightest hesitation crept under my open hand. Perhaps someone else had tamed him (later I learned that this little fellow was a male), but I doubt it, for at that time I knew of no one among the farmer neighbours who was interested enough in birds to feed or tame them in the cold winter days. I think that he was one of those rare birds without an instinctive fear of man.

Not only had he no fear, but his confidence was so great that he felt he could impose his will on me. These little birds, these chickadees, are so persistent when they come to know one well—come to know who carries around their favourite tidbits—that they sometimes almost tire the one who holds them dear. No matter how busy one may be, no matter how cold the bare hand in bitter winter weather, the persistent calls and teasing of these winged fairies for one more seed is never stilled. So at times as I walked along the lane each day going for the mail (the lane runs almost entirely through the wooded ravine for well onto a quarter-mile), I ignored all the flock. Then Deedee—they are all Deedees, of course, to those who delight in them, yet his name seems to be a special one to me—more insistent than the others that he had not yet had enough, would sometimes fly almost in my face as though to stop me in my tracks. Often I felt his little wing gently brush my cheek. Who could resist? What matter the cold bare hands? Deedee must have his way.

Of course he did not want all those seeds to eat. Most of them he coveted to hide behind a piece of bark, in a sumac-berry cluster or other suitable place. At times that suitable place was not only a peculiar one, but one he seemed to have fun in selecting.

One day, as I stood treating his little flock, he seemed to tire of the sport of carrying off seeds and finding safe places in which to hide them. He came to my hand and stayed there a moment looking up at me and if mischief did not enter that tiny head then my knowledge of mischief is nil.

He picked up a sunflower seed, looked up at me, then tossed the seed to the ground. Sometimes a sunflower seed looks sound but is empty. A bird does not have to open the husk to know there is nothing inside. I thought the first one or two he picked up and discarded were unfilled. But he picked up five more seeds and threw them on the ground, each time looking up into my face and calling a saucy "deedeedee." Then, instead of throwing down the sixth seed, he flew up to the lapel of my coat where he clung while he hammered the seed out of sight in the buttonhole. For a moment he clung there, looked right into my eyes and if what he uttered was not a laughing "deedeedee" then it was as close to a chuckle as a bird ever came.

In over seventy years of familiarity with birds, never before or since have I seen another performance like this. It was so odd for a bird that I can see every movement he made as clearly today as I could in that day long ago. There have been many of these sprites since, but this one little bird remains a picture I shall never forget.

Some quarter of a mile to the south of the sanctuary lies a wooded ravine, and there a few years ago was the home of another black-cap whom I came to know well. During one of his wanderings, in early October, he had found the suet-filled coconut shell, and he and the little flock with him joined the others whose home was nearby.

Now raw peanuts, not sunflower seeds, were the treats that they craved, and these I carried mostly in an overcoat pocket. Perhaps all the others knew where these peanuts were kept, but this little fellow was quite sure that he knew. Once as I put my hand in for

A boy's ruthless destruction of their nest cast adrift these baby chickadees

peanuts, he alighted on the edge of the pocket. I held this pocket wide open so that he could see right to the bottom. He peeked in, saw the treat, and after two or three false starts climbed full eight inches down to secure what he saw I had there. From then on for the rest of the winter I had only to hold open the top of a pocket when he was around and the invitation was never refused.

Late in the spring I missed him and wondered how far he had gone, for I did not know then that his home was so far to the south. As at times I wandered around in the woods, I would call with the call we all use for the black-caps and quite often one of these would respond, but never the pocket Deedee. Then one day I visited that second ravine in which I had not been for so long. I called "Deedee" very loudly several times and in the distance heard the unmistakable chickadee note. Then I saw him and held open my pocket—in a jersey this time—and straightway he came, and went in.

Several times more that summer I paid him a visit and, although it was a long time between calls, he never forgot. Once in late summer I had to call loudly and long. For a while I was afraid some enemy had been smarter than Deedee, but suddenly I heard his call as he came toward me. He must have been quite far away.

26

Sometimes I tried to coax him to come all the way to my home with me. He was quite willing to come to his pocket just so far as the trees. But as I walked over the meadow he began to refuse. For a short distance he came, but his hesitation became greater the farther I went. He called often, made short flights from the trees toward me and returned. He wanted to come but did not like the looks of that meadow. He knew in his instinctive way that in this treeless space there was no place to hide.

The next winter he and his family left their home in the far-off ravine for my home. At once he resumed his habit of coming to my pocket for peanuts. When next summer arrived friends of mine found Deedee's nest near the lower part of his old home in the ravine. Seven tiny babies could be seen deep down in the dark hole in the stump. Next day again we went to his nest. The small stump of a tree had been torn clear across and not a baby was left. We were never to know what had destroyed his whole family, nor did we ever see Deedee again. How glad I was that in that last winter motion pictures had been taken of Deedee going right out of sight in my pocket.

Two years ago the third outstanding chickadee came to liven the days of our winter. He, too, as well as the rest of the flock (there were nineteen of them here and fifteen came to my hand), knew that I was the bearer of good things to eat. One day as I sat near the window I held half a peanut close to the glass. This deedee whom we called "Tapper" clung to the sill and pecked hard on the glass in an effort to secure this dearly loved treat. I opened the door, called and held out my hand half full of kernels. Several times during the following day I repeated this teasing performance so that I might learn how long it would take him to realize that a peanut behind glass was not his for the taking.

Another day as I stood near a window I heard sharp taps on the glass. There was Tapper clinging closely, although no peanut was there. I held one up between finger and thumb and again he rapped hard. Could it be that instead of a call note he was using a signal? Most birds do not use mechanical signals, or so we are told. Here was a rare opportunity to learn if that assertion was true. I opened the window and gave him his treat. Off he flew, but in a short time he was back again and began tapping. As he tired of hiding the peanuts I gave him he wandered off into the woods, but each time he came back he tapped on the glass—never anywhere else—to signal that he wanted some more.

Often I tested his powers, for he seemed far more clever than the others. In the living room very large windows face south. To the east of the window is a door which opens onto a closed porch. Outside, between this eastern window and the porch door, are thick-growing arbor vitae. If the chickadee tapped on this window and I moved as though to open the door, he flew through the cedars and waited in front of the porch. He was quite unable to see me as I went from the room to the porch door, yet he knew where to wait. If, however, he saw me walk toward the west, he knew that there was a small window which would open, and he stood waiting on a wild grapevine until I opened the window and held out my hand.

Like all other chickadees he was so persistent in coaxing for peanuts that often I wearied and tried to ignore him. But the more I disregarded his signals the more often and harder he tapped. If I still overlooked his demands and went from this room to the kitchen at the back of the house, the same tappety-tap-tap greeted me there. No matter which room I entered, in time he would find me and he was not backward in letting me know. There were times when I wanted to write, or lie down and read. But wherever I happened to be those sharp eyes sought me out. Little tyrant that he was, it was seldom I resisted.

He was too busy all summer to care about peanuts and, although his mate's nest was close by, he never tapped out his signal again until fall. Then I found that his memory was long. Spring and summer vacation had not dimmed in the least the knowledge that tapping on glass was a sure way of attracting attention.

Was it not odd that he alone, of some thirty or forty chickadees in two years, learned and continued to use a self-taught device for securing a much desired food? May these fairy birds ever be with us, for the woods would be lonely indeed if our "deedees" were not there when we called.

Chickadees like peanuts

Can Birds Reason?

Lassie the collie was lying asleep on the back veranda—apparently dreaming, if one could judge by her twitching tail and cantering paws. Buster the magpie, and Dinah his mate, could see her from the ground and that twitching tail spoke to them of mischief. The middle name of magpies is mischief and no opportunity of indulging it is lost. I wish I had been closer to them when they first noticed Lassie asleep, for, had I been, I am sure I should have seen Buster wink at Dinah.

Without a sound both hopped up the steps, and Buster, alert and wary, stole closer and closer to Lassie. He was caution itself. It must have taken him a full five minutes of vigilant approach before he gained courage to give the end of Lassie's tail a nip. With a start she awoke, looked surprised (for Buster was so far from her that he could not have been the guilty one who pinched her), then went back to sleep.

That nip was such a successful joke that Buster tried it again. This time Lassie was suspicious, for, innocent as Buster looked, this time he had not jumped back so far. Lassie turned around facing both birds and slept again.

Now Buster and Dinah circled behind Lassie and quietly sidled close, alert, ready for instant flight, and nipped her tail. This time, Lassie, with her suspicions fully aroused, sprang up with bared teeth and drawn lips, but both her tormentors were beyond reach. Again she curled up facing them and apparently went to sleep; but I could see a slightly opened eye, and as the magpies approached she was ready for them. It is hard to fool a magpie though. They were taking no liberties unless she was sound asleep. I think that often she pretended sleep, for each time they approached she turned to face them.

29

Undoubtedly Buster and Dinah were enjoying this new game, and from time to time for nearly two whole days they made her life miserable. But she was too wary and they were not satisfied. There were far too few nips. She had become so annoyed that she snarled each time she saw them coming up the steps. This would never do if they were to have their fun. I wish I knew what then went on in those clever heads, but I do know what followed. Notwithstanding that some say there is not room in the head of a bird for eyes and reasoning brain, those two worked out a plan whereby their fun continued—for a while at least.

In the afternoon of that second day as Lassie was lying, apparently asleep, I watched them come quietly to the veranda floor. No sooner had they reached the top step than Lassie turned around to face them. But she did not know that she was face to face with two such imps. Now watch them closely. Buster does not even know that Lassie is on the floor. He wanders around behind her quite unconcerned, with not a thought of pestering in his mind. But Dinah—she is going to peck Lassie right on the nose. Lassie waits with lips drawn back, and instantly Buster rushes in and nips her tail. Lassie whirls and Dinah nips. At last a perfect combination!

Lassie put up with this as best she could but learned in time that she was thoroughly outmanoeuvred. She would stand their plaguing for a while and then retreat to a place on the veranda where they would not go. After all, although she had to give her place in the sun to those pesky rascals, usually she deprived them of their fun—for as soon as she saw them alight she knew their intent. She knew, too, that the only way to cope with them was to seek a place where they would not follow.

Me—First, Last and Always

Robbie has been with me for many years, ever since she was a supposed lost nestling. Curiously, she was slow to learn that if she was to get her share of all good things to eat, she must assert herself. How well she has learned this last few years! Until she is satisfied, and that seems seldom, the food dishes belong to her and should another robin, yes, or any other bird, dispute her right, that most expressive tail expands until one almost thinks her anger is located there. Always there is food for her and many others (if I do not forget for a little while), but that is not the point with Robbie, or her kind, or any kind. In the words of the old song: "I want what I want when I want it; I eat when I'm hungry, I drink when I'm dry." Birds as well as men say, "Me, first, last and always." The cause? Is not the cause selfishness, basic to both, in both uncontrolled? Some time ago a visitor remarked to me about some species, "I do not like them so well now when I see how extremely selfish they are." Do not blame them. They are lovable still. Selfishness is innate in them as it is in most of us, the difference being that we can and they cannot control it.

Can there be a relation between selfishness and caution? Caution is a characteristic of birds as it is of humankind. It varies too in degree, as it does among the various races of man.

You will see how Yak, the white-breasted nuthatch, and his mate exhibited such extreme caution that, although they gave me a modicum of trust for many years, their caution always outweighed this trust. Constant vigilance was theirs; thus their lives were long.

For six years, Sammy, the wild blue jay, and his mate have made their home nearby. Three years or more ago I learned that both had become addicted to the peanut habit, doubtless taught by Deedee and his crowd. Sammy knew well from where the peanuts came and often

31

watched when I treated chickadees and nuthatches. Perhaps from the latter he learned how he could secure more than his due share. Yak and all the nuthatches were expert in catching a peanut kernel when I tossed it into the air. Although he never lost his caution, at times, three winters ago, Sammy secured a peanut when I tossed it far to Yak. Before snows had gone he had become bold enough to stand in a nearby tree and dive for the nut I flipped to him. But I had to flip it. My hand must not move in a toss.

Another winter and Sammy, never throwing caution to the winds, never less alert, began to dive closer to my head for the well-loved treat. I must be very quiet, still, for any sudden move brought instant flight. Before spring arrived he had learned that an opening door meant peanuts. Often he was waiting now when I left the house and my movements, if I was not too close, did not disturb him.

Now, in the deep of a third winter, Sammy often calls when he hears an opening door, catches a peanut three feet above my head and, if he misses one, screams as did old Dick and the first Uno as he retrieves it. This exclamation shows perhaps the acme of confidence in a wild blue jay. In a matter of another three years or more he may overcome his caution and alight upon my hand—but I doubt it. Blue jay cautiousness is too deeply ingrained for that. He may become bolder, but never less cautious; for by caution a blue jay, as well as a nuthatch, lives long.

Sammy's mate is just as fond of peanuts as is Sammy, but she has never allowed her love of them to overcome her wariness. High in a tree she stands to this day; watches Sammy's acrobatic performance as he hangs for a fraction of a moment upside-down in the air; but she has no intention of trusting, as does Sammy, that enemy of birds—man.

In contrast, the chickadees quickly give their trust—not all of them, but most. They seem alert, yet their lives are short. Is this due to lack of caution? It must be so, for potentially their lives are long, according to banding records; much longer than most of us seem to realize.

Not only is life itself dependent upon caution, but also the likelihood of injury from other than predators. Among birds, as among men, there are the strong and the weak. It is not of physical strength or weakness I am thinking but of—may I say, character? The physically weak among birds do not live long, for they are unable to cope with predation. The strong, alert because of their strength, are able as a rule to cope. Strength among birds is, however, relative. The smaller species must give way to the larger. But among individuals of a species there is almost continual contest for dominance of one over another.

32

Father Takes Over

When we study the habits of birds for the purpose of learning in what way and how closely these habits may resemble our own, perhaps as intriguing a way as any is to watch them solve a problem. The problem of Buster and Dinah was how to give Lassie a nip and yet remain safe. That of Sherr, Rée-e and their mates was how to gain freedom. And there was a problem that Sherr had to solve alone.

Although the male rose-breasted grosbeak shares with his mate the duties of incubating and brooding the nestlings during the day, it is the sole duty of the female to carry on these functions during the night. If, while incubating or brooding, the female is killed, we often wonder what happens to the nest or the young. Does the male take over her duties or does he abandon the nest? For a partial answer to this query we are indebted to Sherr.

To supply his mate with what, in her mind, was a suitable nesting site had not been easy one spring. In the nesting compartment were growing arbor vitae but, although she examined them often, no suitable place for a nest could she find. Why she was so hard to please I was unable to tell, for suitable sites seemed plentiful. But she must have her way, for she knew if I didn't. I tied cedar branches together, fastened them up in various places and she examined each one with great care. One, hung in a corner, was selected at last and her nest begun; but she built it right next to the wire. This wire divided her compartment from the main flight where unmated birds were kept in the summer.

Two or three blue jays, Dick's young, now had their home in this main enclosure and I saw possible trouble ahead. The jays I had had through the years never robbed nests, but I did not know yet what these young ones would do. So to be safe I fastened a large shingle back of her nest so that the jays would be unable to see it.

Sherr the rose-breasted grosbeak feeding two of his nestlings—fear is dawning in the nestling at right

One morning I paid her the usual visit, found the shingle on the ground, one of the newly hatched nestlings and one egg missing and many feathers scattered about. It must have been that I had not used sufficient care in fastening the shingle and it had fallen during the night. That dislikable trait so apparent in some jays had possessed one of ours as soon as he had noticed the nest. Her nest, an egg and two newly hatched babies had been strenuously defended by Sherr's mate, for not only were her feathers scattered around but I could see where many had been pulled.

She was so upset, so exhausted and possibly injured (although I could find no serious injury when I examined her), that she did not leave the compartment all day. Nor did she brood or attempt to feed her remaining nestling.

When I replaced the shingle Sherr took his place on the nest, as is the way of the male grosbeak. After brooding the chick for some twenty minutes, he sang—the signal song is usual as a partner returns—and called his mate to come and relieve him. She paid no attention but continued to arrange her plumage as she had been doing all this time. So many feathers had been pulled she probably felt smarting skin. Soon Sherr became restless and left the nest to seek food outside for the chick.

Until their feathers have grown thick and warm, grosbeak nestlings are not left uncovered for more than a few seconds at a time. Sherr's mate should have been ready to cover the naked baby the moment Sherr rose from the nest. Yet here was the tiny day-old chick left unprotected and subject to chill. Now followed incidents which should

35

cause us to pause and consider. Some say birds are not consciously adaptable to sudden change; that they are not conscious as we are of any of their activities. I wonder!

Many times I had tried to breed rose-breasted grosbeaks and this was the first time there seemed a likelihood of success. I was worried when I saw that Sherr's mate refused to warm the little one, so I stayed. It seemed only moments until Sherr was back with several tiny worms. With only a little coaxing he induced the chick to gape and very, very carefully placed the chewed-up insects into the gaping throat. Carefully too he awaited nature's response and then settled on the nest.

Many, many times that day Sherr left the nest for the woods and returned. Each time, before leaving, he became restless; he sang the signal song but his mate did not respond. Usually these grosbeaks when seeking food remain away for a considerable length of time, sometimes for many minutes. But Sherr's visits to the trees were short, at times not more than moments. In some way we do not know, he knew that that baby would not be warmed while he was away and that he must not stay for long.

Dusk came, and with it came the crisis. As I have shown, it is never the part of the male to brood the young during the night. Sherr sat on the nest; called, and again, as so often before, sang the signal song; became increasingly restless; left the nest often, stayed off for a few minutes and returned. His mate made no move to take her accustomed place for the night. Once, when he was off, I took her in my hand and placed her close over her nest, but she refused to stay. She had had a bad fright, and that peculiar and important rhythm of nesting was broken. Too, she may not have been as adaptable as Sherr, for he, as it darkened, settled down over the nestling for the night. I know, for I stayed until long after dark.

Next day Sherr's mate still made no effort to attend to her little one and Sherr carried on double duty. Fearing that she might go off to the woods and wander away, although this was unlikely, I carried her to the main enclosure. As another day dawned, she coaxed so hard to get back through the wire to her home that I let her in and put her on the nest while Sherr was off seeking food. She looked at the youngster but refused to settle down on the nest. In the hope that her maternal instincts would be roused, I gave her small mealworms and tried to persuade her in other ways, but her interest had gone for good. There was now only one thing to do; put her back with the unattached birds.

Although restlessness seized Sherr each evening at dusk this restlessness became less and less and in a few days disappeared. It was for him to take on the duties of father and mother and not once did he fail. For

36

Sherr (in winter plumage) being fed by the author

nearly thirty long days he sought food for himself and the youngster. He warmed it and fed it and kept the nest clean. By now the little one was little no longer, was nearly as large as his father and ready to seek his own food. Surely Sherr proved his adaptability to change. How can we say with confidence that instinct only ruled?

Merul, the European blackbird, and his mate had a different problem to solve. A metal dish six by eight inches and two inches deep contained water for drinking. To keep the birds from fouling the water, a cover of metal with flanges to fit over the side was placed on top of the dish. The back half of the cover was flat and the front half bent up. This formed a canopy which allowed them to secure the water they needed. To keep the cover in position the flanges were made to fit snugly. When filled with water the dish was placed on the floor and *close to the wall*.

After much use, it was apparent one day that the flanges had expanded a little, for, as I watched when Merul hopped onto the canopy, the cover tipped down, thus closing the pan. Of course, the back of the cover tipped up, but since the pan was close to the wall, Merul was unable to reach the water when he wanted a drink. He walked back and forth over the cover, hopped down and up several times and examined it carefully, then suddenly put the tip of his bill under the canopy and lifted it to its normal position. At the time I wondered if his mate also would be able to solve such a puzzle. Therefore, instead of tightening the flanges, I left them just as they were so that when either hopped to the top the lid closed. After watching I saw plainly that the solution had been deliberate, for each time the weight of a blackbird lowered the cover and either wanted a drink, the cover was raised by its bill.

Perhaps you will say that my interpretation is wrong, that raising the lid the first time was an accident and they learned quickly. If so, why did Merul examine so carefully and often the closed lid? Unquestionably he knew that the closed lid must be up if he was to drink. Then if he bent down his head, as he did, and pressed upward—well, I shall leave that up to you.

Black and White with Rosy Vest

"Sherr-ee-e. Sherr-ee-e." From some forty feet away came the velvety-soft, quivering notes—the location notes of ten-day-old rose-breasted grosbeak youngsters. These were sleepy notes. The little heads were low in the nest, for a short time before their mother had been there with a full bill of brown and green caterpillars.

Ten minutes passed. One baby raised its head above the edge of the nest and there came the same entrancing call—perhaps the most entrancing note of any baby songbird—this time a little louder than before. A little pang of hunger may have been in that call. More minutes passed and four heads showed above the rim where one had been before. Hunger notes became clearer, more insistent, as neither father nor mother appeared with food. I was wondering by this time: a little worried, for I knew that that enemy of small birds, the Cooper's hawk, was nesting about a hundred yards away. So I stayed to watch. Full twenty minutes passed and still no parents. I understood why the mother had not come: she was busy with her second nest. These first nestlings were in almost full charge of the father, for she had visited them seldom these past few days. To judge by their almost frantic calls, the youngsters were starving. Stretched to their fullest height they were literally screaming for food.

Now happened what I have seen but once in almost a lifetime of interest in birds. For many years I had been under the impression, fostered by authorities on birds, that the rose-breasted grosbeak reared only one brood in a season. I wondered. There was much to be learned about the life history of these birds: much that was not known and which could not be learned from birds in the wild. For these reasons I had hand-reared several rose-breasts some few years before. Now, nesting in two compartments of the bird observatory, two pairs had built their nests. In No. 1 compartment, that of Sherr and his mate Nara, were three young, of the same age as the four hungry ones in No. 2 compartment, the home of Rée-e. The gate to liberty in No. 1 was facing east; the gate in No. 2 was facing west. About thirty feet separated the two entrances. In No. 1, too, the father was in charge of the youngsters, for his mate likewise was busy with her second nest.

Sherr, the father in compartment No. 1, had been visiting his youngsters with food every few minutes. As the calls became louder from No. 2, I noticed him pause for a second on his platform and glance at the hungry ones, but he too had three hungry youngsters to feed and it was not his place to take care of those of his neighbour. Feeding one family is a full time job for a single parent. It would seem, though, that even a bird *may* have the same compassion we can feel for hungry children. Just over my head, from the top of a tall tree, I heard his greeting song as he approached the observatory. As I looked up at him he flew to his entrance gate, paused there for a second and looked at the screaming youngsters. Apparently there was no resisting those cries of hunger. Upward to the top of the observatory he flew, across and down to the little gate on the other side, and straight to the nest. Carefully—how carefully these birds do feed their young—each little bird got a share, for his beak was crammed with insects. No tarrying there at the nest however for, had he done so and the father had returned while he was there, there would have been severe punishment for his trespass. His own little brood went without their share, as they did several times.

Some time afterwards the neglectful father entered and fed his young. It was a puzzle to me why he had remained away for such a great length of time. The mother had built her second nest too far away for her to hear readily the cries of her nestlings; or perhaps she was asleep on her nest, for often they have a daytime sleep while incubating.

When Rée-e, the father, left the compartment I decided to follow him. He flew straight to a ravine, over a hundred yards away. That seemed odd, for his territory did not extend in that direction, nor were the boundaries so far away. As I approached I could hear him singing in the wooded ravine but I could not locate him. Farther and farther away to the east I could hear his song. I kept following the sound and at last, some two hundred yards from his nest, I saw him—and could hardly believe my eyes or ears.

His voice now was the courtship song, so different from the territorial, so entrancingly beautiful that words cannot adequately describe it; and his courtship displayed an exquisite tableau. He spread and

39

drooped his rapidly quivering wings so low that the tips of the primaries grazed the ground on which he stood. His body was held in a crouching position with the breast almost touching the ground; his tail partly spread and slightly elevated; his head retracted so far that his nape lay against the feathers of his back. The mating song poured forth from his open beak as he moved toward the female, weaving his head and body in an erotic dance. The downward and forward sweep of his wings revealed in striking contrast the blacks and whites of the separated flight feathers, the vivid rose of the underwing coverts and the white of the rump. The song was soft, low and continuous, with a great variety of notes. Some of the sweetest were inaudible, for I was twenty feet away; yet in my mind I heard them clearly. Often before, this courtship song had been sung at my very feet. For pure rapture I cannot recall any song which quite equals the courtship song of the rose-breasted grosbeak, unless it is that of his cousin the black-headed, which is similar.

All this wonderful display and song for whom? For his mate? Not at all. Here was the answer to his neglect of his youngsters. An unmated female had wandered through his territory and—have we not heard the story often before?—wife and children were forgotten as he pursued for a while this new and ravishing beauty. Perhaps his own handsome self (he was the most beautiful rose-breast I had ever seen) brought out the philanderer in him. Handsome as he was she seemed to pay no attention and, apparently discouraged, he returned to his family. Not once again did I see him neglect them.

Often I took nestling food to the young in both nests, for I wanted them to know me. Eagerly they took the food offered on the food-stick. Should Rée-e happen to be in the compartment as I approached his nestlings, he would fly at me, screaming; for he was always an untamable bird. He did not trust me at all. If I offered food to the nestlings when the mother was there, she showed me plainly that she did not trust my feeding methods by snatching the food from the food-stick and giving it to one of the youngsters before I could do so. If I happened to get the food into the mouth of one, quickly she would take it out and place it gently just where she knew it should go. She did not mistrust me in any other way. I might handle the little ones, take them out of the nest to measure their growth, or stroke them. That did not worry her a bit.

When they were younger and she was brooding them, if I offered to touch them she did show that she preferred that I leave her babies alone by taking my finger gently in her bill; but that was the extent of her objection. On the other hand, Sherr and his mate had the utmost confidence in me. I might lift either off the nest to examine their eggs; take the little ones out to examine their down; or, after they had become old enough to take nestling food, might feed them as often as I wished. Both would go off to the woods and leave me alone with their fledglings while they collected the green caterpillars so dearly loved by these birds. Should a young bird be on my hand when one of them returned, my finger was used as a perch and the little one fed where it nestled.

When the little birds were about twelve days old and had begun to climb about the arbor vitae planted in their compartment, the parents decided it was time for them to leave their home. It was fascinating to watch them call and coax the youngsters onto the entrance platform, and then out into the wild. But it left me in a quandary, for I wanted to follow the lives of these little birds and I could do so only while they were in the observatory. Several times I caught the little ones that had been coaxed out and replaced them in the compartment, but sometimes, also, it was very difficult to find them. As there were seven in the two broods I found that I had more on my hands than I could handle. It became necessary to devise some means of keeping the youngsters in and at the same time allow the parents to supply them with the very necessary live food which they could secure only outside the observatory. Here too was a splendid opportunity to determine the intelligence of these birds.

"Sherr's mate had the utmost confidence in me"

The platform in the gateway was a four-inch-wide shingle extending some five inches into the compartment (the compartment itself being enclosed by one-inch-mesh wire). Using mesh wire, I made a three-sided cage which fitted over the inside platform and four inches above it. The sides and end of the cage were two inches away from the platform and also extended two inches below on all sides. To gain the platform the grosbeaks would have to fly down from their perch and then up between the wire and the shingle. This cage proved an obvious puzzle to Sherr who was there when I adjusted it. When he attempted to alight on the platform which he could see readily, he alighted on the top of the cage. First he tried to get through the wire and attempted to do this a number of times. He stood on it, examined it, trying to find some way out; then back to the arbor vitae. Often during the next five minutes this examination was repeated. Then suddenly, he flew under the platform, up on the inside of the cage to the shingle—and freedom!

Shortly afterward his mate entered and fed the young. Then the same performance was repeated by her. I timed her also and found that she took almost ten minutes to solve the puzzle. Once solved it remained solved. None of the young ones, however, were able to find their way out—I too had solved a problem. When I placed the cage over Rée-e's platform, it was solved by him and his mate in almost the same length of time.

Although both Sherr and Rée-e were singing lustily and occasionally Sherr and his mate came to me for a favourite food, neither second-brood nest could be found for some time. At last I saw Rée-e's mate fly to the top of a tall hawthorn; twenty feet up, in the very top, the nest could be seen. She was left undisturbed until it was evident she was feeding well-developed young. Then the tree was cut and lowered a few feet each hour until the nest could be viewed readily. In it were three youngsters about eight days old. Gradually the nest was moved closer and closer to the observatory and on the second day it was placed in their compartment where the parents soon found it.

Now happened the only tragedy of that entire season. On the second day after moving the nest I watched Rée-e preening his feathers in a tree some twenty feet away. A little later I noticed that his mate alone was coming to the observatory with food for the young. This time it could not be that he was philandering with some strange female, for the season was far gone. The Cooper's hawk! I searched the woods, and there on a stump some hundred yards away were the feathers of Rée-e, freshly plucked from the beautiful body.

Day after day I searched the woods for Sherr's nest, without success.

It is unusual for these birds to build at a height much more than twelve feet from the ground, exceedingly unusual for them to build very high; so I had no thought of watching the treetops for the nest. His song seemed to come always from the treetops, though the canopy was so dense I rarely saw him or his mate. At last, over three weeks from the time she had left to build her second nest, I saw Sherr's mate fly into the very top of a large beech tree with worms in her bill. With field glasses the nest could barely be seen, fifty feet up in a crotch. Obviously it could not be reached.

Nara—unconcerned as the author examines her youngster

On the end of a long stick a wire hand was fastened; a great length of string tied to a paper bag, and the climb to the very top of the tree began. With the greatest difficulty the nest was detached and placed in the bag. When the bag was lowered and the nest examined one baby bird was in it. When I looked around, there on a branch ten feet away was another which had jumped from the nest and floated down. This little one was secured, placed in the nest and the nest fastened to a three-foot branch which I stuck in the ground. After several visits to the top of the tree, the parents heard the location calls of the nestlings, and came to them with food. Gradually, by many short moves, the nest was taken closer and closer to the observatory. When it was nearly there, I noticed that Sherr alone was bringing food to the two young, although his mate could be seen not far from the beech, carrying food in her bill. Coax as I would, carry her in my hand to the nest as I did, she would not stay and feed the two little birds. At first I could not understand. Then—the possible explanation: another little bird had come down and had not been seen. Carefully the mother was followed, and on a twig not far from the beech was the baby. How close I had come to losing that little one! Now, because of the hawk, it was best to close the whole family in their compartment for the season.

Now her second brood also was reared in the observatory. Complete success had crowned the efforts to make an intensive study of these birds for a season, marred by only one misadventure. Almost three months' liberty had been theirs. Thirteen young (nine males and four females) were reared to maturity. Thus two pairs of semi-captive birds had hatched one hundred per cent of their eggs and reared one hundred per cent of their young. Rarely do birds in the wild have such success.

For the first time, so far as we have been able to learn from the records, it was discovered that rose-breasted grosbeaks would rear two broods in a favourable season. An unusual demonstration of what we know as compassion was given by a bird. Proof too of what we call reasoning was evident. And we gained other valuable knowledge about one of our most beautiful birds, and one of our finest songsters.

Russet Back
and Speckled Breast

There are hawks in the blue; there are owls in the dark of the night; the creeping, slinking weasel at dusk or dawn—nature's methods of control. These are not the only hazards with which we have to deal, we who are trying to "add to the knowledge of the ages." The chill of night, the sudden and lasting storm—and the entity that is a bird: with these we have to contend. We know so little of what goes on in the mind of a bird, what its reactions will be to an unexpected or unforeseen event. Nature has given to them what we may call the nesting rhythm. To upset this rhythm is so easy, their reaction so often unpredictable, that we make many mistakes when we attempt to give help to those in our care so that they may carry out nature's succession of duties. The gamut of intelligence varies so greatly between species, between individuals even, that often we are faced with indecision, and the decision made is as likely to be wrong as right. Nowhere has this been more true than in the sequence of events following the mating of that wondrous foster mother of another year, Vee the wood thrush. Yet, with all my mistakes, I gained knowledge I did not have before.

One June when there were fifteen nestlings to be reared together in a small enclosed porch (three bobolinks, three cardinals, two Baltimore orioles, one cowbird, three wood thrushes and three veeries), Vee, then a young unmated bird, had helped me to feed this varied nursery. It had been entrancing to watch the stirrings of motherhood take form. I can still see that little foster mother running, running all day long, never pausing to rest, or even to eat, it seemed, until the little ones began to peck, then to feed themselves. These were her babies—all fifteen—despite the various species they represented.

45

A day in the spring of the year following Vee's upbringing of the fifteen, brought first slow pulsation to the throat of one of our male wood thrushes. Quietly I approached to within a few feet, and, listening carefully, heard a gentle warble, slow and leisured, as is the way of our wood thrush. As the days went by, the song evolved, and by early March the rich, flute-like notes poured forth in dignified deliberation. Whether or not this song was for Vee I do not know. As Vee had sisters there, it may have been for one of them; but to me it seemed that he was singing only for her.

For all Vor's glorious song, his was not an ardent courtship. Like his song, it was deliberate; dignified to a degree. None of the exuberance of the grosbeaks; no display and erotic dance for him. Not that he was not excited, for he was. But he showed it more by "cresting" the feathers of his crown, by magnifying his beautiful spotted breast—all for her admiration. Slowly he approached her, crown feathers raised high, a single flip of his wings and a short, sharp "quirt, quirt" and—not much more. Yet this little seemed to be effective. Certainly, before the month of May was very old, Vee had chosen him to be her mate.

It was too late for the move to the summer home. The cold and rainy days of almost all that month of May made it dangerous to move the birds from their well-heated winter home. But Vee had been anxiously searching for nesting material for some time—with little success, for I cannot allow the birds to nest in the winter home. Too many of them are interested in mischief (pitching the eggs and young out of the nest) for any nesting bird to be successful in rearing young. So Vee and Vor were moved to compartment No. 4. This new summer home was large and in it grew white spruce, with branches thick and firm to hold a nest.

Skeletonized leaves—leaves from which all but the ribs and veins have been eaten by caterpillars, leaves as light as feathers—are much desired material for a wood-thrush nest. These I hunted for where the witch hazels grow, and gathered many from there. Vee also needed mud to bind together the leaves and to form the deep cup. At the foot of the lawn was a little ravine and mud—robin mud. A quantity of this I gathered there and placed in a box so that it might be kept wet and plastic for her. No sooner has I placed these materials in her compartment than Vee became intensely interested in the leaves, turning them over and pitching them to one side. Perhaps she was only looking for worms, but, no—suddenly, with head held side-wise, she gazed into the top of the seven-foot spruce. There was no mistaking that look in her eye. There—was a place in which to build

46

Vee the wood thrush on her nest in the spruce tree

a nest. Up she flew, hopped from branch to branch, quietly examining each likely site. Once, before she flew down, I saw her settle herself in a favoured spot, spread and flutter her wings as though trying it for room. Her decision was made, for she picked up a billful of leaves, flew into the spruce and placed them just where she thought they should go. Some were dislodged as she put them in place, but these favoured leaves were retrieved.

Some mud now was needed to hold the leaves together, so Vee went to the mud box to test what I had brought. She dabbed at it with her bill, threw some aside, and tried another place. Then she looked at me as though to inform me I should know that that was not the kind of mud a wood thrush uses. Over the years an intimate association with trustful birds induces quick understanding of at least some of their actions. At once I knew that Vee would not use that mud. I hunted up a swampy place and gouged out the mud and wet leaves of the woods. This was what she had wanted: wood-thrush mud, not meadow mud.

47

Early in June her nest was finished with no help at all from Vor—not that he was uninterested. Often he examined her unfinished work. But the flute in his throat was his main contribution.

After her first egg was laid Vee and Vor were not at once given their liberty—the liberty I usually give to nesting birds at this time. There was a real reason for this. Wondrous songsters as they are, beautiful in dress and lovable in disposition, their little brains sometimes do not function on quite the same plane as that of some birds.

Perhaps I misjudge them. Maybe it is only that they are less observing, less careful to mark the path to freedom in their minds, or, perhaps their memory is shorter than that of some others, although I doubt this. Whatever the reason, when they return from the woods, the little gate seems always hard to find at first. To Vor it is most important that he should readily find his way to the close vicinity of the nest, for he must stand guard when Vee leaves to feed and drink and bathe. If he cannot find his way in, the rhythm of nesting may be upset. This may not, however, be nearly as serious as for Vee to be unable to locate the entrance gate the moment she comes back—for she too will find the little gate in the compartment and go out to hunt the delicious caterpillars she has been without for so long. Too soon her eggs will chill and then—no babes.

There was just as real a reason for *giving* them liberty at this time—so they could become used to finding their way in before the eggs hatched. If, when Vee's eggs hatched, she became confused and could not find the entrance gate, thus being unable to cover the chicks, they too would chill—and die. I felt sure Vor would have no difficulty in finding the gate, for he had learned so well the year before, but nature did not assign the task of covering the young to the male wood thrush. Much as it would distress him to see them left uncovered for any length of time, the power to take the place of his mate was not an inherent part of him. Of course, there was another solution for me—a dangerous solution. I could take down the outer mesh wire in its entirety. But should I do this, then the prowling cat, the weasel, hawk or owl, could readily enter the nesting compartment—as I have good reason to know. Then I would lose not only the little thrushes, but Vee and Vor as well. What would you have done? Day after day I debated with myself—there had been similar misjudgments in other years—as uncertain and undecided what to do as was Cherree, the evening grosbeak mother, when she placed the twig crosswise in the mouth of her baby.

At last I decided that I should give them liberty the day the first egg hatched and watch carefully so that I might help Vee to find her way in. Early one morning in the middle of June I opened their gate. Almost at once Vor found his way out.

Fortunately for Vor—and for me—bluebird Josie, who for some unfathomable reason, had an intense hatred of wood thrushes in general, and a particular animosity toward Vor, was not yet ready for liberty. Vor and his mate of another year had hatched their young at the same time that Josie and Little Blue had hatched theirs. There were plenty of insects for the food of both broods, and for others. But not one of them belonged to Vor, according to Josie. Should Josie be out of her nest and spy Vor in the grass or among the leaves or shrubbery, searching for food for himself or his young ones, all thought of her nest was forgotten. Her vicious attack drove from him most of the thoughts of *his* nestlings.

Vor was no coward as he had proved well in the past, but the onslaught of this bunch of blue feathers in female attire was too much for him. He skirted the edge of the trees in full flight, Josie ten feet behind; around and around the meadow, a good thousand yards, till he dove into the woods out of her view. All that month and more, with plenty of food so close to his home, he did not dare linger so near.

This was not more than comical to me—until I found that he was seeking most of his food in the long winding lane. The lane is a quarter-mile long, twisting and turning through the wooded ravine. Basswood, the favoured home of the measuring-worm, was plentiful here. A motorcar meant nothing to Vor. A car coming round the bend, Vor a few feet in front, a sudden screeching of brake, did mean something to me. I placed a sign near the end of the lane, asking that cars be slowed down and drivers be watchful for a little brown bird unafraid. That was an anxious season, but Vor came through quite unscathed.

Vor leaving his gate to seek insect food for his young

Now, in this other June, Vor did not need to seek his natural food so far away. Twenty minutes of liberty satisfied his wants—or did it? Perhaps it was something more important than bugs and beetles that brought him back so soon. Perhaps you would like to judge.

Incubation of the eggs and brooding of the young of many species is the sole duty of the female. Whether or not the male knows when his young have hatched by seeing them in the nest, or knows in some other way, has been a controversial question among many who study birds. You who read may decide.

It was ten o'clock in the morning on the fifteenth of June when I opened the gate of exit and entrance. After his short search for grubs he returned and at once found his way in. Memories of another year remained to tell him the way, for in that other year he had had great difficulty in locating the gate when first given freedom. Only once during the next two and a half hours did he leave his compartment and return.

All afternoon I stood by the nest, watch and notebook in hand. Every move by either bird was watched: when Vee turned the eggs; pecked at the tiny, widening openings in the shells, or merely looked at them; when she left the nest to eat or to drink or to bathe—each event was entered in the notebook minute by minute. Although she trusted me well—not so well as did Vor—I had to stand very still or she would at once cover her eggs with her breast. Only part of this long record will be of interest to you. Let my notebook give these parts, so that you too may judge of the way of birds:

At almost exactly twelve twenty-five Vee leaves her nest. As I stand close-by I can see a pinpoint hole in one of her eggs. Vor flies to the rim of the nest and looks at the eggs, as often he has done before. Vee returns to her nest after being off for less than a minute, then later stands up in the nest and pecks gently at what must be the tiny hole which at present I cannot see. As she settles once more on her eggs she utters a low note, apparently calling Vor to the nest. He hops to the rim and I hear a low conversation between them. Vor's bill is full of saliva which he appears to want to give to the nestlings that have not yet hatched. Vee refuses to rise and Vor gives her some of the saliva. She then rises sufficiently to allow him to look at the eggs. While he is watching, she pecks at one which now shows a hole about an eighth of an inch in size. It seems apparent that before she called Vor she felt the moving beak of the unhatched chick, and called her mate at that moment. Vor shows excitement by continually erecting the feathers of his crown. Most certainly he did not see the unhatched nestling, but he knows that it is about to emerge from the shell.
It is the middle of the afternoon. Vor has been in almost continual song. I move a little closer and can see that one nestling is entirely out

50

of the shell. The other is still in the shell, which has separated all the way around except for a quarter of an inch. This nestling is moving continuously and can readily be seen. The one entirely out is throwing itself around in the nest. Vor does not go near, but is excitedly running and flying around with crown feathers raised. It would seem that he knows that the nestlings have hatched without seeing them.

As Vee drops the empty shells on the ground, Vor finds a soft-bodied worm which he masticates with his bill, then flies to the nest. After considerable coaxing to induce the nestlings to gape, he feeds it to one. Although this is the first time Vor has seen them, he knows they are out of the shell and ready for food. Does it not seem, not from observation, but from communication, that he knows of their birth? I have been watching him carefully and not once, for over an hour, has he been in a position where he could see into the nest.

Vee leaves her nest and finds the open gate. While she is out, Vor stays for the most part on the rim of the nest. Minutes pass. This is the crucial test and an anxious time. Twenty minutes have passed and Vee is flying around the observatory, trying, without success, to locate the entrance. I touch the eggs and find them becoming cold; take them out of the nest and place them under Sherr, the male rose-breasted grosbeak who is taking his turn on his nest. Then I take the two nestlings to hold and warm in my hand. Vor is much concerned when I put my hand into the nest. As I hold his babies he murmurs low notes as he gently touches my fingers. He seems anxious, is singing, apparently using this song to call Vee to her young. She responds by flying distractedly round and round the observatory, unable to find her way in.

Just as Vee is opposite the gate Vor flies in front and she sees the entrance, runs through, and while I am placing the little ones there, flies up to the nest. She looks at the babies a moment, then warms them. Only four times this late afternoon does Vor leave the compartment to seek food for the young, and each time he comes in, it is necessary for him and for Vee, with whom he divides his billful of food, to coax long before the little mouths open. Does it not seem like an error, that, as some would have you believe, such feeding reactions in the parents are excited only by gaping of nestlings? Here seems definite proof that that *is* an error, at least so far as the wood thrush is concerned.

Early next morning I give back to Vee one of the eggs I had put under Sherr, and in the afternoon, both it and her fourth egg, still under the grosbeak, have delivered their young. Sherr's mate is exceedingly careful in removing part of the shell which is sticking to the head of the baby. She pulls it a little then lets it drop, then pulls it again. Seven exceedingly gentle pulls and off it comes. She seems to know that it should not be pulled off with a jerk.

Sherr and Sheree his mate, both of whom are hunting their food in the trees, are trying to feed the new baby, but without much success. Their feeding methods are so different from that of the wood thrush: they are so careful that the swallowing muscles should grasp the food; they

51

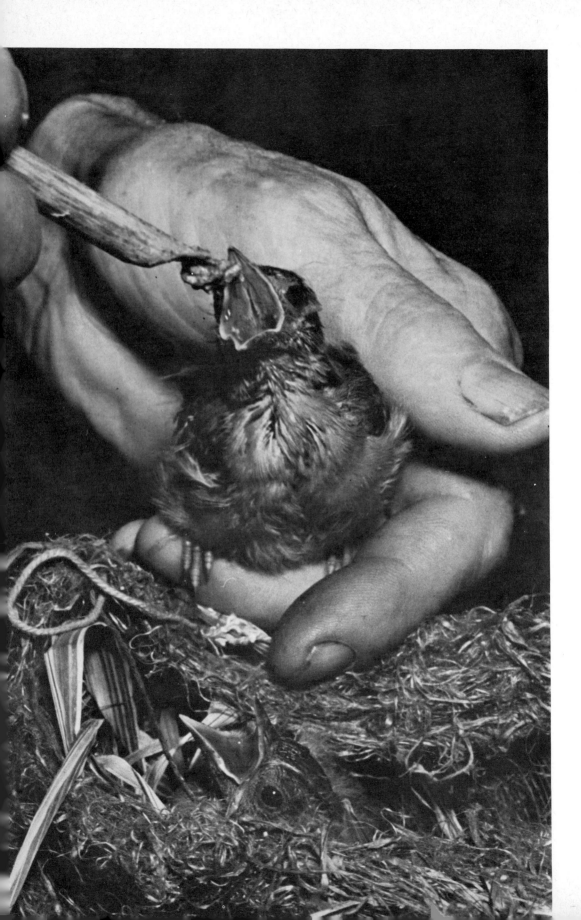

give and withdraw it so often that the little thrush is too tired to gape further, and thus remains unfed. Both try again and again, but without success, so in the early evening I take the baby from them and return it to its mother.

The second morning is cloudy and damp and chilly. Heavy rain has been falling most of the night and morning. When I enter the wood thrush compartment and look into the nest, all four nestlings appear dead. Vee must have gone out very early and been unable to find her way in. I take the babies to the house and revive the three oldest, by placing them in a nest in the oven. When they seem fully recovered I place them in their nest, as Vee has found her way in. Apparently she has been in for some time while I have been warming her little ones; but her finding the nest empty has broken that strange nesting rhythm. Whatever the cause, she will neither feed them nor brood. But Vor flies to the nest with food and tries, with much coaxing, to feed them. They are seemingly too weak to open their bills for the food he has brought. Several times, as I find they are chilled, I take them to the house to be warmed; and three times, when I put them back in their nest, Vor tries to feed them, each time without any success. For the fourth time I have placed the young in the nest, but now neither Vee nor Vor offers them food, although both go often to the nest and look in. Both are much excited and worried; are carrying food in their bills; are running around on the ground as though hunting their nestlings there. There is one thing only to do: take the nestlings into the house and try to rear them myself, an almost impossible job with babies so young. I gather soft-bodied caterpillars and place them deep in their throats and they swallow, but nestlings so young seem to need the parents' saliva as well. Before evening has ended all the little thrushes are dead.

Neither Vee nor Vor left the compartment again that day. Each kept hunting all over the ground, flying often to the nest to look in. For eight days both carried food in their bills, visiting the nest in the expectation of feeding babies which still should be there. Some "authorities" say that a bird's memory is short: that the loss of their young or their mate is not felt. Would this not seem to prove they are wrong? Usually when the nestlings in a nest are destroyed, the birds build again. Vee seemed to have lost all interest in nesting, for she did not even attempt to build another nest, so I closed the pair in for that year.

Now as I write, in the middle of winter, I hear Vor calling—the sweet wood thrush note. I leave my work and go to the mesh wire partition. He flies from the far end of the winter home for the ground peanuts he knows I have in my hand. And Vee? Just as likely as not she is on the storeroom floor, hunting for the spiders she knows she will find. She is always under my feet when I work in the storeroom: the moment I open the door in the mesh wire partition, she darts in. How I wish she wouldn't do this, for each step I take must be watched. I must not forget for even a second. If I do, little Vee would probably hunt for spiders no more.

53

Baltimore oriole nestlings

Gold and Bronze and White

Montana came out of the west; the southwest it would seem, for instead of the great bill of one of our most brilliant and welcome winter visitors, his was the smaller bill of the southwestern evening grosbeak. Therefore we named him "Montana," which later we shortened to "Tana." "Vesper" was a golden bird of the north, and he too had come to reside with me not so long ago. "Tina" had been with one who had been studying evening grosbeaks for many years but she knew me well, for this was her other home. "Cherree" and "Beauty" were old, old friends, for they also had been with me many years.

Early in May of a year gone by, many of the birds—those which showed a desire to nest—had been moved from winter to summer quarters. This summer residence is an octagon, with large nesting compartments surrounding the main flight. Compartments No. 1 and No. 8 were reserved for our grosbeaks. They would have many neighbours. In No. 2 were the wood thrushes, Vee and her mate Vor, with their three feathered young; in No. 3 was Robbie, the male robin; in No. 4, White-ring and his mate, the rose-breasted grosbeaks, with one nestling out of the egg; in No. 5, Little Blue and Josie, the bluebirds, with five newly hatched babies; in No. 6, the catbirds, Fuss and his mate, with four youngsters almost ready to fly; in No. 7, Sherr, the eight-year-old rose-breasted grosbeak, whose mate was incubating her eggs.

In June of that year, Cherree had accepted Tana as her mate and No. 1 compartment was to be their home for the season. Then Vesper mated with Tina, and they were provided with compartment No. 8. Ideal nesting sites were ready in the growing arbor vitae.

As all my efforts of the past had not led to successful nesting, it was decided that as soon as the pairs were formed, nests built, and the first

54

eggs laid, the four evening grosbeaks would be given the same liberty as was given to all the other nesting birds, so that they could seek natural food among the trees. The exit and entrance to the compartments would be by the small gates in the outer mesh wire, similar to those used by the other birds during the season of nesting.

Now began a delightful experience: a prelude to the beauty we would see often during the next few days. The male evening grosbeak is an exceedingly handsome bird. The large areas of golden yellow, shading to umber-bronze, stand out in striking contrast to the black and white of his wings; but to see him in all his beauty he must be seen as he courts his mate a few feet away. The wide-spread and rapidly vibrating wings, the elevated tail and retracted head, the erotic dance, all so like the courtship postures of the rose-breasted grosbeaks, make perhaps an unpaintable picture. Yet his mate, like so many of her sex, does not seem nearly so impressed as we; or if she is, she does not show it, for she goes quietly about the business of building as though he were not there.

Neither Tina nor Cherree were at all satisfied with the nesting material first given to them. Never having seen an evening grosbeak's nest, nor being aware of the nesting material they use, I had gathered various twigs and rootlets which I scattered on the ground in their compartment so that they might choose for themselves the ones they thought suitable. But the twigs of various kinds were picked up and discarded: none seemed to suit. It was then suggested to me, by a student of grosbeaks, that I try supplying them with the same kind of nesting materials they used in their far northern home. I collected brittle pine twigs, then ripening shepherd's purse from which the seed heads were stripped. These latter, cut into six-inch lengths, and the pine, were scattered on the ground. Now building really began. Even though Cherree had been with me many years, she had not forgotten the essentials of nest-building. Later I supplied them with many fine, thread-like rootlets of shrubs, and these they used for the lining.

The nests of both pairs were finished. In each the first egg was laid. Now the small gates were opened and soon all four found their way out. Excitement was rife; incessant calls to one another were heard as they explored the many trees and the wooded ravine. For an hour or so the new-found freedom was enjoyed, then Tina returned to her nest, while her mate Vesper, and Tana with Cherree, explored farther afield. Then disaster! Vesper failed to return. Did a sharp-shinned hawk, suddenly, like a bolt from the blue, streak with terrific speed from the woods? We do not know, but we do know that Tina had a mate no more.

Hand-reared female cowbird in the winter observatory

Rarely do these hawks nest in this district, but it was now evident that a pair had located within hunting distance as Josie, the mother bluebird, and later Sherr, the old rose-breasted grosbeak, were taken. Continued liberty for the grosbeaks was now out of the question for this season. Tina's gate was closed. A little later Tana and Cherree returned to their nest and their gate too was closed. Our experiments would, for this year, have to be carried on under the old and hitherto unsuccessful conditions.

Three more eggs were laid in each nest. We hoped that Tina's would hatch even though the last three were laid after Vesper had disappeared. But whether they were fertile or not made no difference to Patsy, the female cowbird who had her summer home with many other birds in the main flight compartment. She was determined to give Tina another egg to take care of, and all her spare time—she had plenty—was given to trying to find an opening in the mesh wire large enough to squeeze through. Her persistence was rewarded, for at last she found a broken wire, a wire which later took us hours to find, and —well, we found one of Tina's broken eggs on the ground and Patsy inside the compartment!

Anxious were the days now on account of the sharp-shinned hawks; the fear of prowling cats; yes and human feet, for the catbirds and wood thrushes sought most of their food on the ground, and the thrushes in particular, having no fear, would suddenly appear from nowhere right under our feet.

Yet with all the anxiety, the seemingly never-ending care of this busiest season of the year, we had beauty at its best, beauty of both sight and sound. The home of our birds and the woods about were full of glorious song, and calling—and baby notes: babies calling for their food. Also location notes, and the soft whispers of the parent birds as they brought food to the ever-waiting mouths; the soft warble of Little Blue as he brought food for Josie's young, and the quiet signal song of Sherr's mate as she saw or heard him in the distance, coming home. Then suddenly, dead silence, each bird "freezing" where it stood. A glance upward, and there, a speck in the sky, a hawk so high there could be only amazement at a bird's perception. Utter silence broken only by the warning notes of the bluebirds, or Tana's "whee, whee." The danger passed—suddenly all was activity and calling and glad singing.

In due time two of Cherree's eggs hatched. A continual hunt for insects and ant larvae was now in order. Fortunately these grosbeaks enjoyed earthworms, although they were almost as difficult to find as insects on account of the drying earth. None of their favourite seeds were given to Tana and Cherree as it had been found in former years that these would be fed to the newly hatched birds with disastrous results. However various nestling foods were supplied and these were relished not only by the parents but considered by them quite suitable for their babies. But with all our care Tana and Cherree were able to rear only one of the nestlings.

It was almost time for the little fellow to leave the nest when the urge came to Cherree to rear another brood. She carefully examined the old nest; decided, apparently, that a little building up of the edge and some new lining would make it as good as new.

That the baby was not quite ready to leave the nest did not seem to bother her. Tana was doing most of the feeding now, so Cherree had time on her hands—or should we say on her wings?—and seemingly an overpowering urge to hurry before it was too late for a second brood. She began taking up rootlets which she carefully placed on the inner edge, then moulded them with her breast. With the big youngster in the way this was a difficult, if not impossible, feat and she was not making rapid progress, much of the new nesting material falling to the ground.

To prevent such interference, an experiment on our part was necessary, one which might or might not work. The quandary was this: if the baby is left where he is, not only will the mother have difficulty in rebuilding her nest, but, dissatisfied with her efforts, may lose that important urge—important to us at least—to lay again. Or, if the unfeathered little one, who still needs his mother's warmth, is moved to another home, Cherree may refuse to follow him even if this new home

57

is only a foot away. If this should happen, the morning would find only a still, cold form. One has to be exceedingly careful about interfering with the rhythm of the nesting season. Perhaps it would be best to leave the nestling with the mother for a little longer at least.

That evening at dusk, when I paid my last visit of the day, I found Cherree all ready to sleep, twelve inches or so under her nest, leaving the baby uncovered and cold. Do not blame her too much. Perhaps I was at fault. Possibly I had fed him so often she had decided she would leave him entirely to me. It would not be the first time such an experience had come to one who had intended only to help. Dick and Pet, in a year gone by, had told me so plainly in their own blue-jay way, that if I was going to take care of their babies, then, I could take care of them. And they meant it, for they just would not feed them and I had to rear them myself.

There was Tina, and her baby bunting! Perhaps she would take care of another one at night. Gently I lifted the little fellow from his nest and showed him to Tina. She gazed curiously at him and, as I placed him beside her, she seemed uncertain and puzzled for a moment. Then as the baby snuggled close to her side she arose slightly and allowed him to creep under her breast. (I shall tell you later how Tina had got her baby bunting.)

Rather late the next morning I put him back in his nest, but neither Cherree nor Tana noticed him there. Held in my hand, I showed him to them, then lowered him into the nest. At once each went to the food dish for the food they knew he should have. During the morning Cherree had built up the sides of her nest with pine twigs and shepherd's purse stalks, but now that she wanted to line it the baby was again in the way. A new home for the youngster seemed the only way out. An abandoned robin nest fastened close to the old nest should make a satisfactory home for the little fellow. After the robin nest was relined with grass the young one was placed in it. Now the refinishing of the old nest went on with more speed.

Cherree, however, did not neglect her baby and in between times gave it a billful of food. To feed him and to refurnish her home had an equal appeal, and this led to a conflict between two desires—and also to a most comical incident. As she flew to the nest with a pliable twig the nestling called loudly for food. Cherree hopped to his side and he gaped, ready for the food his mother should have in her bill. Cherree wanted to feed him and she wanted to use that twig in her nest, but could not make up her mind which to do. Back and forth between the two nests she hopped in supreme indecision. Then as she stood on the side of his nest, still undecided, looking first at her nest and then at the

58

baby, the youngster continued to gape; so she placed the twig cross-wise in the wide-open mouth. This did not solve the problem at all. At once she saw her mistake, took the twig from the mouth of the baby, and hopped again to her nest where she laid the twig without attempting to place it just where it should go; then flew down to the food jar. After all, her baby came first.

Interesting and enlightening as is much of the newly observed behaviour of birds, rarely do we see such a comical incident. Cherree's confusion brought a gale of laughter from us who were fortunate enough to see such a droll situation. But Cherree did not mind. She was too busy to consider our mirth; even if she had not been so busy, probably it would have had no meaning for her.

Fearing that if Tina were forced to become a foster mother to the nestling grosbeak it might result in the little bunting's being neglected —it was so very small—the young grosbeak, now named "Oro", was taken into the house at dusk and placed on a hot-water bottle sur-rounded with cushions. In the morning, before returning him to

Sherree, female rose-breasted grosbeak, chooses a twig for her nest

59

Cherree, I fed him twice. Fear was just dawning, though slightly yet, and he drew back a little when I offered him food. But, as I talked to him, memory of my voice returned and quite readily he accepted my offering.

Now for the first time, when back in his nest, he took his initial exercises by rapidly vibrating his wings. Cherree fed him and cleaned his nest of fresh droppings, as is always the way of a bird with its young. Then she continued relining the old home with fine inner bark of white cedar and very fine roots of twitch grass. And Tana took over most of the task of the feeding, for Cherree still seemed anxious to finish her nest. Next morning there was an egg in that nest. For five nights the hot-water bottle was mother to Oro; then he needed a covering no more, for his own warm feathers would now keep out the chill of the night.

Another morning and Cherree's nest held a second egg. When I visited, Tana was on the edge of Oro's nest and he and Cherree were holding a conversation. He hopped over to the rim of her nest as she hopped off to allow him to peer at the eggs. As he peered, he uttered low notes which she answered. Tana soon became more interested in Cherree and her eggs than in Oro and the mother had to do most of the feeding. When not feeding Oro or herself, Cherree was incubating her eggs. Even so, Oro came first, for she appeared more fond of him than did Tana. Once, when she was off the nest seeking food, Oro hopped on the edge and then in. Five times Cherree went to the nest, intending to cover her eggs, and looked in; seemed puzzled, reluctant to move him. Fearing that her eggs would become chilled if left uncovered too long, I lifted him out and she settled down on the eggs.

Two mornings later there were four eggs, but still Cherree fed Oro. Tana and I fed him too; but now, although Cherree did not mind my handling her baby, she was beginning to object to my feeding him. As I offered him food, she uttered a low single note, then took the food from my fingers and gave it to him. The days passed; and Oro, now almost as large as his father, had learned the art of feeding himself. Nestling food and such insects as could be gathered had given us our Oro: our first nestling of his kind in many years of endeavour.

Unfortunately this second nesting of Cherree was unsuccessful. After all, Cherree was old: too old to be a successful mother twice in one season. But we had learned something seemingly unknown before, that evening grosbeaks sometimes nest twice a year. Too, we were successful in rearing at least one nestling to maturity—this for the second time in the history of captive, controlled grosbeaks.

60

After Patsy the cowbird had found her way into Tina's compartment and had stolen and broken one of her eggs as is the way of the cowbird, Tina continued to incubate those that remained. When, after fifteen days, we found that no youngsters had hatched, we took the eggs from her. She objected to this: would not leave the empty nest. She was quite sure little ones would appear if they were given time. Of course she did not tell us this. Perhaps she was not sure at all. Perhaps she was just sitting there, waiting, waiting. We do not and cannot know. We do know that she was ready: that nature had prepared her; for we made a plan and she accepted it as she would not have done a week or more before.

The eggs were given back to her for a little while. Then we hunted and hunted for a nest in which there might be newly hatched nestlings. Only one could be found, the nest of an indigo bunting; and that held babies so small that we had grave doubts about Tina's being able to feed and rear one, for her bill alone was almost as large as one of these little ones. We hesitated long before taking one of the tiny birds to her —that baby bunting mentioned before—but she was such a lovable, gentle bird, had lost her mate such a short time ago and now was about to lose all her eggs; we decided to try the experiment. We must watch closely and, if it was seen that her bill was too large for the little mouth, the nestling could be returned to the nest.

Tina did not fail. She was as gentle and careful as though it was one of her own, perhaps more careful because it was so small. I tried to help her and she did not object. Food was accepted from me as it would have been from her mate. Part of what I offered was taken and fed to the baby, and I was supposed to put the tiny remainder in the wide-open mouth. In fact she seemed, for the first few days, to expect me to bring the food to her as her mate would have done had he been there. Once I gave her a little caterpillar which she chewed and rolled around and around in her bill. When she was satisfied that this tasty morsel was thoroughly prepared, she let me have part so that I might put it in the mouth of the baby. That was not so surprising as it might seem, for complete co-operation is the avian way.

In time our baby bunting acquired a coat of darkest blue. We had given Tina a bird's happiness and ourselves the rarest treat. Another season of interesting experiments had passed. Our efforts had been well worth while, for new lore had been gathered about these somewhat peculiar and little-known birds: knowledge that cannot be gained in the wild. Not only Tana and his kind, but rose-breasted grosbeaks Sherr and Nara were to teach us more of the ways of our grosbeaks.

61

A baby cedar waxwing says he is hungry
(on the author's shoulder is an elderly female rose-breasted grosbeak)

Ori, the Oriole

Ori, the female juvenile oriole, was sick. She had been staying, since an orphan nestling, in the large sunroom observatory (adjoining my living room) in which were the warblers, tanagers and other highly insectivorous birds. This observatory, eight feet wide by twenty feet long, is heated in winter by an electric radiator and the temperature kept at about sixty degrees. Three large plate-glass doors separate it from the living room. When I found her unwell I put her in a cage over one of the baseboard electric heaters where I could keep her in a temperature of about ninety degrees.

When she recovered, after some weeks, she had become too used to the greater heat of the living room to be put back in the sunroom. Therefore I gave her the liberty of this room for the rest of the winter.

All our songbirds are exceedingly fond of mealworms. These are bred in a cabinet placed in one of the closets off the hall leading from the living room to the kitchen. Ori learned where these worms were bred. She learned more than that. When I intended to give her a treat (one must not feed too many of the rather tough-skinned worms) she must have watched me, many times, going to this closet, and she has remembered. Now, when I get up from my desk and walk towards the hall she flies to my shoulder in the sure expectation that I am going to the work cabinet. In the evening the hall may be dim and the closet pitch-dark. No matter: she clings to my shoulder until I turn on the light—and she gets her desire.

Ori is exceedingly fond of coffee, a drink that may be harmful to her. Should I be lying on the couch in the evening with a cup of coffee on the stool beside me, she is sure to fly to the stool and then onto the rim of the cup to dip her slender bill into her favourite drink. I do not deny her a single dip but that is all she may have. I place my hand over

63

the cup and she tries to pry my fingers apart. This will not work and I warn her that she must fly away. Now here seems to be where learning begins. I warn her by words that she must keep away from the cup. It would seem that she knows by the tone of my voice that she is on prohibited ground, for she flies hesitatingly to the edge of the stool, pauses there, creeps closer and up to the edge of the cup. I say commandingly, "Ori get off" and she immediately —sometimes—flies off.

On the seed tray and on the author's left hand are female Baltimore orioles— on his right hand a male catbird and an alighting bluebird

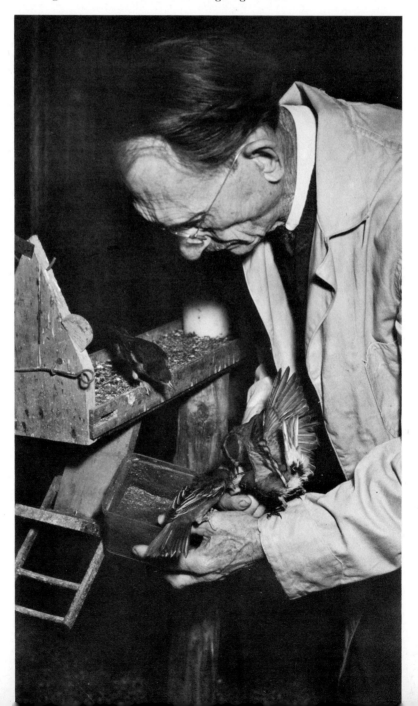

Black Cap and Grey Cap

It was deep winter. Through the window I was watching those delightful little fairies of the air, the black-capped chickadees, as they rapidly tap-tap-tapped at the frozen suet with their tiny crowbars. There was suet on the window ledge. The white-breasted nuthatches knew the suet was there; had been enjoying it as a treat since early snows. As I watched, a nuthatch came flying from a nearby oak straight toward the window sill. Suddenly, midway, he dropped like a stone to the snow where he struggled on his back, unable to rise. There were no hawks in sight; no apparent cause for his fall.

I ran out, picked him up and brought him to the house. He did not struggle in my hand and I thought him dead. But he was not limp, and two bright, black eyes stared into mine. I saw no signs of injury, no blood upon his feathers, nor were these feathers even rumpled. I stretched his wings; there was no break in them. Then what was wrong? To this day I do not know.

I held him close for a little while, then carefully felt along the slender cord that was his neck. The thought had come to me that in some sudden turning of his head he might have dislocated a tiny vertebra. This might be the cause of the sudden paralysis. Again I pressed with gentle fingers, trying to locate some hidden twist; then placed him in a closed and ventilated box. After almost an hour had passed I quietly lifted the lid. He seemed as well again as when I saw him upside-down upon the oak. There was nothing further I could do but let him have his trees once more. His mate was there and he rejoined her in perfect flight. It was two decades and more ago when it happened—that peculiar accident, if accident it was.

Yak and Yak-yak: down through the years as one pair succeeded another, the names never changed. There was no need for change.

65

The songbird sanctuary and surrounding woods, large as they were, usually had room for one pair only of white-breasted nuthatches: our "upside-down" birds.

In the long, cold winter days sunflower seed as well as suet had become a favourite food for both chickadees and nuthatches. Rarely did I leave the sunflower seed upon the sill—these were my early days of living here and I had no feeding stations then—but carried the seed always in my pocket, handy for the several chickadees who had learned to alight upon my hand. Yak knew I had these seeds. The black-capped elves hid many in the crevices of the bark of trees and in the sumac-berry clusters and these were surely found by Yak and his sharp-eyed mate. Their keen black eyes did not fail to note that I was the bearer of this welcome treat.

Coax as I did in the early winter, not once could I entice either to come even close to where I stood with seeds on open palm. Not even the wary blue jay is so alert, so cautious, so careful that no enemy may see him first, as our queer little white-breasted nuthatch. For this reason, perhaps, none of our other songbirds has so long a life in the wild. Then what was my surprise one morning when I stood beside a tree to see Yak come "inching" down the bark, head-first, toward my open hand!

I held a sunflower seed between my thumb and finger, my hand against the tree. Closer and closer he crept down, then in sudden panic darted back and around to the other side, quite out of sight. Still as a statue I stood, calling gently "Yak, Yak"; and cautiously, oh so cautiously, he came around the trunk in spiral movement towards the wanted treat.

In low voice I repeated the name I had given him. But not yet was he ready to trust me. He must know for certain that mine was a friendly hand. When an inch away he paused a moment, then rapped me hard, several times in succession, on the tip of my thumb. The thumb never moved. That was all he needed to know. Gently he took the seed and, in the peculiar way of a nuthatch, hitched up the tree to a broken stub where he hammered the seed into a crevice, then proceeded to take off the husk.

Now that the ice was broken Yak often came creeping down the trunk, although for most of the winter he did so with great hesitation. Not once again did he need to make the test of friendship: the sudden striking of my finger to see if that finger could be trusted. Soon, when I appeared outdoors he began to call me with an odd, nasal voice so different from the usual "quank-quank" of these birds. This call appears to be one not used when talking to his mate, for never have I heard it except when a nuthatch has been coaxing for some favourite food. To me it seems that they use it only for their human friends.

Before the winter was old, Yak learned to alight on my hand, but more often—it was not his nature to give his trust outright—he clung to the edge of my palm. Yak-yak also knew that it was I who carried those favourite seeds, but there was no coaxing her to my hand. It took two winters' persuasion before she too gained sufficient confidence for that, and it was not until the third winter's snows that she came to alight on my hand. Perhaps, had we been intimate friends throughout the year, she would have gained that confidence sooner; but when nesting-time came, these two were too busy to be bothered with me and my gifts. Only rarely did I see them from late spring until fall. Usually they nested too far away in the depths of the woods.

Each year both Yak and his mate became tamer. Now they would follow me through the long winding lane when I went for the mail, calling and teasing for more favoured food than sunflower seeds. At first they had looked suspiciously at the small, raw peanut kernels I offered, but once these were tasted the sunflower seeds lost much of their former appeal. All the way up the lane and back they would follow and it seemed that every few steps I must pause to satisfy their insistent appeals. Not that they always wanted these tasty morsels to eat at the time, but to hide. It is the way of the nuthatch to store each bit of such food they do not immediately eat in various suitable crevices, or behind the rough bark of trees.

With all their tameness, neither one, in all the years they remained with us, ever gave their full trust. That is not the way of the wary white-breasted nuthatch. For days, as I watched them come to my hand when I called, it would seem that their whole trust was given; then, for no apparent reason, sudden shyness would come. Perhaps for ten minutes or more I would coax and entreat, but much as they wanted to come, some hidden fear held them back. A peanut or two, tossed in the air, was caught by one or the other in a dexterous way; then suddenly, once more I was their trusted friend.

They were songbirds, had their own charming ways, and our woods would have lost for me some deep attraction if they or their kindred had not been here. But Yak—and all the later Yaks who, throughout the years, have let me learn their ways—had one peculiar trait that jarred. Except during the nesting season Yak was an irascible tyrant where his mate and smaller birds were concerned. Always in *his* mind he came first, and did Yak-yak dare to alight on my hand or close to me when he was near, he drove her off with vicious lunge and threatening voice. Not only here but in the trees, if she was close, he would make a sudden dive at her as though to keep her in her place. He meant it too, although I never saw him strike her; and she understood, for she never disputed his right. Yet each must have been fond of the other for rarely were they far apart. I have a feeling, though, that she could stand this mastership of his for just so long, for a time would come in winter months when she would part from him for as much as three whole days. Then, when he alone would tease for the nuts I wanted both to have, I would worry for fear some enemy had captured her. Suddenly she would reappear, and again for long these two would search the woods together.

When spring was far advanced, what a change there was in him! Hesitatingly, he lost his domineering ways. A day would come when the peanut from my hand was taken up the tree and gently offered to her. How solicitous he now became for her welfare! He was as gentle in his ways as earlier he had been mean and selfish. Always I was able to know when this change in his disposition was due to show. Or at least I thought I knew, for as soon as I heard Yak-yak's voice change from that we knew so well to a softer, more pleading—yes, more pleasing— note, I expected Yak to forgo his domineering ways. Doubtless he heard the change in her voice before I noticed it, although I am not so sure of this, for I learned to know them well.

Yak-yak the old female white-breasted nuthatch

Now Yak followed her wherever she went. A whole summer's respite was hers for the taking. Her way was his will and the complete co-operation of mated birds, so necessary for the welfare of their race, was evident in all their ways. Their nest was built, their young were reared, then driven off. Each youngster must hunt up a home for itself. The thirty-odd acres of woods were large enough only for Yak and his mate. Until a more dominant pair should come to drive them out, this was their exclusive home so far as their own kind were concerned. Sometimes they would rear another brood and these too must leave. Now Yak-yak must resume her subordinate place in the scheme that is their lives.

Winter after winter passed and after several years I began to notice a growing change in the plumage of Yak-yak. Each autumn the change was slight, but sufficiently noticeable so that I began to call her "Old Lady." Most of the change was in the feathers over her eyes. These grew longer and lighter in colour. Now too, when each spring arrived and these two disappeared for weeks at a time, I would wonder, "Will Old Lady be with us again next winter?" I know that the lives of our songbirds are short, perhaps not more than a year and a half on the average; yet these two had been with us for years more than that. Each fall, in early October, the suet was ready, and a warm glow suffused me when Yak and Old Lady called me often again.

The tenth fall arrived since first I had known them. Old Lady was old that last winter, and during the following summer the rare times I saw her I noticed a change. She was not so alert in her movements; looked aged and grey. "How long yet shall we have her?" I wondered. Then Yak and his mate one day, from the tree-tops, came calling, but —his mate was not Old Lady.

At long last we had lost her. Often I wished that during their old age I had given a home to this pair. Yes, she must have been old, very old, when she left us. Yak showed no change in his plumage, although at times I thought him a little less active, less domineering: so she must have been much older than he. Perhaps she was fifteen or sixteen—or twenty. Who knows!

Another October arrived and I heard the nasal twang of nuthatches. I called, "Yak, Yak," but there was no response. I threw a peanut high up in the air. Neither paid any attention—I was totally unknown to them. Somehow I knew I would never see old Yak again. All their long lives together he had been faithful to Yak-yak and she had been faithful to him. Now I must try to make friends with the new.

This new Yak and Yak-yak soon learned there was suet for the taking, watched the chickadees alight on my hand for the peanuts which always were there; but it took nearly two winters to induce them to trust me. Old Yak's domain became theirs, but late in the winter of their third year here another pair came and disputed the right of Yak II and his mate to this woods. Oddly, these new ones soon became tame; early gained the confidence it usually takes two years or more to attain. For a while there was much flashing of wings and angry notes when the two pairs happened to meet near the suet container. Then one day as I watched, a battle began, the two males in combat quite close to where I happened to be, while their mates fluttered round, each threatening the other yet never coming to blows.

It was not a fight to the finish by either, but was a contest to decide who should remain. To me the battle seemed to conclude in a draw and perhaps it was close to that, but later I found that Yak had had the scare of his life. I found him and his mate in the south wooded ravine a hundred yards or more from my cottage. For nearly a month I tried every day to induce them to follow me home. To the top of the hill they would come, but no farther, yet called to me from the trees when I left them. At long last I did induce them to come, but when Yak *did* arrive he met Yak III. However, in some unknown way he had regained his lost courage and would not be driven away.

Just how the problem for these two was settled I never did learn, but a boundary was set, that boundary my home. Now the south woods belonged to Yak II and the north woods to Yak III. Always after, upon meeting, there was bad language and posturing; but now that the boundaries were drawn the peace was not broken.

For six years Yak and Yak-yak II remained with us, three of this six years in the woods to the south. Then as I watched, a new pair, number four, drove them away and I saw them no more.

Yak and Yak-yak III remained in the woods to the north while the new pair took over the woods to the south. Without any dispute, so far as I was able to see, the old boundary line was retained. The same "hard feelings" were shown when they met, yet apparently there never were blows.

This new pair tamed readily and continued to show me the way of the nuthatch. For a year they seemed happy together, then some serious domestic trouble arose. One day in the middle of winter Yak-yak came to my hand. With a sudden dive from a tree Yak darted at her, angry and vicious as I had never before seen him. Not from my hand only did he chase her, but far into the trees. Then he came back for his peanut and in less than a minute she too arrived. Again he struck

70

Windinglane Cottage—the observatory to the left and behind

at her and drove her away. Not once in the following weeks did I see them together. At odd times she continued to come, and he, often. But if they arrived at the same moment, he not only drove her from me but right out of sight.

I saw her less often and then not at all. For some reason or other it was outright divorce; it was not that he wanted to mate with another, for the rest of the winter he was always alone. In the springtime I saw him no more, nor ever again. A pair, number five, took his place. Even today three years later, not only do they not know me, but they never visit the house where the suet bells hang.

Yak and Yak-yak III had been, during one winter, the most confiding of all and Yak seemed more gentle towards his mate than any before him. Upon the arrival of spring they built in a bird house far back to the north, at the edge of the woods. As I visited this bird home one day I called "Yak" many times, but neither appeared. I opened the lid of the box and looked in. Not an egg could be seen; the top of the nest was flat and I felt sure it was deserted. I took off the bottom and threw the nest on the ground, thinking that if the bird house was clean some wandering bluebirds might find it.

Something over a week later, a student of birds stood on the spot while I lifted the lid to see if some bird had discovered it. Our student, curious to learn what a nuthatch used for nest lining, pulled apart what seemed to be fur on top of the nest I had thrown on the ground. At once I was shocked and regretful, for there in the warm rabbit fur were six eggs. Yak-yak had so thoroughly covered them before she left to hunt food that I had been completely deceived.

Again I lifted the lid of the box and there on a new nest was Yak-yak. I called her by name, then gently reached in my hand and quietly moved her to one side. Six pinkish eggs were beneath her. Softly I let down the lid and we left. Some time later six little nuthatches flew out of that bird house, or so we surmised, for we saw them when they were almost ready to go.

I had left suet out during that summer, for the downy woodpeckers were using much of it in rearing their young. Yak and Yak-yak brought their big family, too, for this treat. Winter came and with it another new pair. As I watched, a battle developed, and Yak and Yak-yak disappeared out of sight. The new pair came back to the suet and I saw the others no more. The new pair are still here, but in two winters I have not succeeded in taming them, although they call me and catch peanuts when I flip them high in the air.

Little Josie Comes to Me

One morning a friend and I wandered down a country lane which ran through unused pasture land. Clumps of alfalfa dotted the meadow— clumps dearly loved by bobolinks for nesting sites. The exuberance of these gay troubadours had been the main attraction that had drawn us on this morning in early May. As we listened to the rollicking out- pourings of the bobolinks, the liquid notes of the song sparrows and the clear sweet voices of the field sparrows, the warble of a bluebird drifted like a low obbligato through the symphony of song. On a fence post farther down the lane a splash of blue stood out vividly against the green of the meadow.

Apparently the little fellow had just come from the hole which could be seen as a shadow on the post some distance away. As we drew near he spread his wings and disappeared as a blue speck down the fence row. Then, as we stood still, his mate arrived and entered the nest.

Quietly waiting until she came out and disappeared in the same direction as her mate, we approached the post for a quick look. There, much nearer to the top of the cavity than usual, we saw five tiny naked nestlings. None could be more than four days old. As we watched them the mother suddenly appeared, alighting on the next post. Protesting notes warned us that she did not approve our presence so near the nest. So we slowly walked away.

Here at this nest would be much of enormous interest, even though we had only the morning hours to visit it. Our visits must, however, be quiet and circumspect as this interest must not interfere with the nesting pair. Our next morning visit brought a hint of coming tragedy—so often met with in the world of birds. A quick look into the nest while the parents were out of sight showed four where five should be. A search of the ground about the post showed no clues to

73

the fate of the missing nestling. It was a puzzle how it could have disappeared. We felt faint disappointment, for bluebirds are not so plentiful here since the starlings came.

Another morning visit and there were only three. Still there were no signs to show why the little birds had vanished. Leaving the nest we sat on the grass a short distance away, not wishing to disturb the parents. For an hour we waited and watched while our binoculars grew heavy in our hands. No sign of an enemy was seen. The parents did not seem perturbed and uttered low notes of protest only when we went closer to search the ground again. We were reluctant to leave, for now there was no doubt that one of nature's tragedies was being enacted.

As we approached the nest after another day had passed we felt trepidation: the fear of what we might find. This fear was justified. The little home was emptying: mysteriously, inevitably. Now only two little orange mouths showed when I touched the nest hole. This was not a pleasant visit, for I felt some tendency at first to rage against the spoilers; yet reflection calmed resentment, leaving a sadness and deep regret. It was only one of nature's methods of control. Much as we dislike to see these little tragedies; much as we would like to prevent them if we could—nature knows best. But such logic does not soften the feeling of sadness when we see this control in operation.

Perhaps it was only fitting that the fifth morning visit should be when the light was dim and the sky weeping as it can in early May. Slowly but surely the little family was being wiped out. One tiny bird was occupying what should have been by now a crowded home. On the next tomorrow there would be an empty nest.

Coming upon an empty nest that has been full the day before can cause keen disappointment. Rarely do we see the actual tragedy itself. Sudden regret is our feeling, and then it passes. But here were we who, if not witnesses to the actual destruction of the family, day by day were seeing the results of the enemy's visits and were unable to prevent the final destruction. Yet possibly there was a way to save the last of the little ones.

Reluctantly the decision was made. We waited until the parents were out of sight, then fingers were quickly but gently slipped into the nest: the five-day-old bluebird, still almost naked, slowly and carefully lifted out. Without a backward glance we hurriedly walked away. It would not be good to see the return of the father and mother to their empty home. To rear successfully a tiny, almost naked nestling (which had been filled each day to repletion—if they ever can be filled to repletion, which I sometimes doubt—with that so-necessary insect

74

food) is a perplexing problem for a person without experience. That experience my friend did not have. A sufficient number of insects could not be secured for this little waif by its foster father, and the substitute food was not producing the bodily strength and rapid feather growth that is normal. It would be difficult for the foster father to part with her, for one gets greatly attached to these appealing little ones. But he felt that someone who knew the secret of feeding would have to finish her rearing.

Thus Josie came to me. Josie—one of the most lovable birds it has been my privilege to care for. The new food soon rounded out the little body and the feathers grew apace. Yet, shortly before she should have been able to fly I noticed that the flight feathers of one wing had not developed. Nor was her mouth the rich orange it should have been, although it was not as pale as when first I had seen it open so appealingly

Bluebird Josie with cedar waxwings

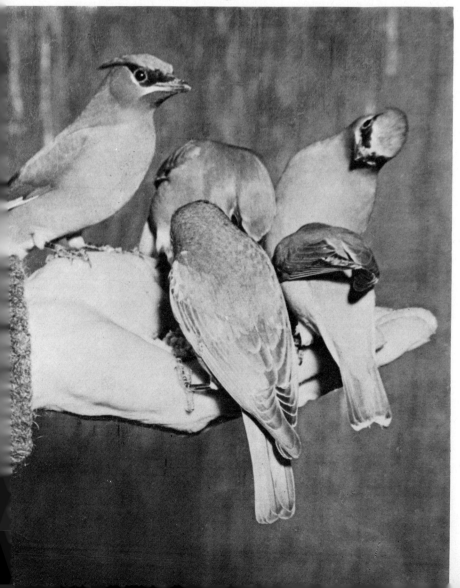

to me. Her lack of flight feathers was to be a source of regret for I must confess to a feeling of frustration when I have a bird which cannot fly. Not to be able to take off and remain aloft for as long as they desire, in that element in which they are so much at home, seems a cruel fate. How helpless such a bird seems and sometimes is.

At last I decided to try to pull out the tiny primaries in the hope that new ones of normal length would grow but, as I pulled one, blood appeared. Then I was sorry that I had tried. I could not bring myself to hurt her more. Perhaps the full moult a few months away would result in normal plumage. In the meantime branches had to be arranged in ladder form in the observatory so that she might reach her sleeping shelf, the food cups and the bath which songbirds find so necessary.

From the first Josie showed all the lovable and fascinating characteristics of all young songbirds before fear develops, or returns. Sometimes I think that little bluebirds and veeries are the most enchanting of all. Yet, when I recall the many others I have reared I cannot be certain of this. Each has its peculiar charm: the wood thrush with that odd sideways lift of the little head as it accepts food; the "bobo" with his weaving head, the mouth so hard to find. Yet somehow, when very young, Josie seemed different from all the others of her kind. The hollow of my hand was always her favourite resting place. Just the way she crept into it was captivating in itself. The perfect confidence; the way in which she held her head sideways and looked straight into my eyes—how odd that birds so often do this—endeared her to me as few have ever done.

Whether or not the extra petting and attention given this little flightless one had anything to do with the lovable traits she developed can be only conjecture. Throughout her life, except during the breeding season, she showed a remarkable attachment to me, not only by desiring to nestle in my hand but by her acceptance of my gentle stroking of her feathers. While her head and back were stroked her eyes would close as though in thorough enjoyment. There was no resentment when she was held, her wings lifted or her feathers parted. "Hands off" is a must with most birds. Such familiarities are resented by even the tamest and most confiding birds with the exception of the crow. Not so with a rarity like Josie.

Five months passed. Josie's moult was now complete. A month before it could be seen readily that the old and tiny flight feathers on the right wing were being replaced by new ones. Now these new ones were growing as well as those on the left: I had the satisfaction of having her fly to my hand instead of having to pick her up.

Red-tailed hawk

Young scarlet tanager and bluebird

Ten-day-old orioles

"Incredible! I still don't believe it." The visitor was leaving. During the hour he had lingered, bluebirds, rose-breasted grosbeaks, wood thrushes and other native birds had come swiftly and trustingly from the treetops, the grapevine posts (I gave them liberty in the great outdoors), to alight on his shoulders and hands.

One of the bluebirds that had delighted the visitor so much was such a hand-reared bird—our Josie. As I have told you Josie had been, since her babyhood, an unusual bird. Unusual in that even among hand-reared songbirds she was one of the exceedingly rare ones who, as you have seen, not only submit to being held in the hand but coax to be so held. More than that, her very life as a nestling had depended upon unusual circumstances.

Many young birds when hand-reared have a return of the fear which usually becomes evident at varying times before they leave the nest, and which often is latent until they become independent. Josie never at any time showed signs of fear of me. Towards strangers sometimes a little mistrust was evident and she would not cuddle in their hands. Her confidence in me was perfect but, more than confidence, she seemed to have what among human beings we call affection. I feel that the deep affection we can know was just as much a part of her as it is of us, modified because she was a bird, yet certainly akin. Why not? And because of Josie I was to learn of another emotion, that of hate, among these gentle birds; and yet another kind of affection that seems to show how closely akin their emotions are to ours.

I have been asked "Why keep such birds as Josie and Little Blue and so many others?" May I tell you why?

The Sky Above and the
Earth Beneath

Joey, Josie's future mate, also was a lovable little fellow with every confidence in me so long as he was free every second, but he would become frantic if he was imprisoned in the hand. He had no hesitancy in coming to my hand, but it must not close on him. He must feel free; his feathers must not be touched, nor any part of him.

For a bird to come to a human hand, rest upon it, take food from it, shows the height of confidence. The hand, to a bird, is a trap. Of all parts of the body it is most open to suspicion. As they become tame the feet may be ignored, the head placed close, without their taking fright, but a movement of the hand causes instant alertness.

Entire confidence often is established in a peculiar way. It may take weeks or years for one to gain this confidence, but with many a bird—usually one which has not been hand reared—a test must be made before it is granted in its entirety. It is a test for retaliation and does not seem to be related to dominance. Slowly or swiftly, confidence is gained until there comes a time when one thing only stands in the way of its completeness.

Some say birds do not think or reason. What else goes on in the head of that little bird as it finally comes closer and closer to the hand, then suddenly strikes hard at, or bites, the fingers which are held out with some tidbit? It seems to be no more than, "Can I really trust? If I am not struck in return I can." Not in our language of course, but the thought processes must be there. Otherwise, why the test? Why the acceptance of the relationship after the test has been made? In that bird brain, small though it is, there is recognition and a realization that the hand and the owner of the hand can be trusted. Joey did not need to use that test, for fear never had returned to him.

As birds vary in disposition they vary in other ways. Joey was more precocious as a baby than others at that time in the observatory. All nestling birds are ravenous: they have to be, to grow at the rate they do. But Joey seemed to love his stomach more than most. He knew that if he did not get the food on the food-stick some other would, and he intended to get it first. He usually did. In fact, all his life when certain bird dainties such as mealworms were being served he saw to it that he secured three or four to every one the other bird got.

As a youngster he was first when the food-stick appeared. He was more insistent than the others that he be fed, yet that did not prevent his following the urge which seems characteristic of many young bluebirds: the urge to feed younger ones of his own tribe. When he was a baby there were no younger ones to feed, but the impulse was there and he must feed someone. It was enchanting to watch the progress toward maturity as this little fellow was on the threshold of independence. Almost imperceptibly adolescence came. Instead of watching the loaded food-stick he began to notice it being dipped into the jar. Shortly, he rested on the jar itself and looked in. Not yet, however, was he ready to help himself. Many times he would see the food-stick dipped before it became firmly fixed in that small head that what he was receiving could as well be had by helping himself.

I think that it must have been on the same day he realized this that he perceived that the other birds also ate food. Just in front of him a goldfinch picked up a seed. While he was shelling it, Joey hopped down and calmly took the seed from the goldfinch's bill—then offered it back to him. Later that same day he stood close beside a rose-breasted grosbeak while it cracked open a sunflower seed. Interest in that procedure was profound and I think that in that instant was born in him the strong impulse to feed other birds.

Shortly after, as I was shelling a sunflower seed for a catbird on my knee, he took the kernel from my fingers and attempted to feed it to this bird. She did not understand what he was trying to do and hopped away. Well, if she did not want it some other bird must. He tried to give that seed to five different birds, none of which understood his intentions, for they were all adults, and not used to such niceties. Not understanding, they retreated from him, thinking they were being attacked. However, there was another kind of bird which would not retreat! He flew to me, clung on my chin and placed the seed between my closed lips. Frankly, I did not want the seed, but Joey was quite sure I needed it. As it protruded from my lips, he began to hammer it with his bill and was not satisfied until he had it hammered out of sight.

What puzzled me then and what puzzles me still is how he, a baby

Bluebird in flight—Takeoff   *Approach*

bird, knew that between my closed lips was the proper place to put that seed. My open nostrils were so close, yet he must have known that there was not where the seed should go. It was quite natural that he should have recognized the bill of a bird as the eating place, but the closed lips! However, mystifying as it was to me, somehow Joey knew.

Joey was one of many birds in the observatory and one of two male bluebirds of the same age, although these two were unrelated. Josie had chosen Joey as her mate very early in the spring of her first year when she was about eleven months old. Perhaps, in fact, she had chosen him much earlier than that, for even during the winter these two had occupied the same roosting shelf during the night. This is a point to remember, for it has a meaning in relation to her behaviour toward me and the affection of which I have written. It has been pointed out by others that tame birds treat man as a member of their own species. That is true, yet it is not necessarily all that their behaviour may imply, for tame birds react differently to man than towards their own kind in many ways.

Each evening at dusk Josie and Joey would fly to the roosting shelf where often there was competition between them for the inner corner. If I entered the observatory at this time Josie would leave her shelf and come to creep along my arm to nestle in the hollow of my hand. When she did this Joey would also leave the shelf, fly to a branch and back to the shelf, time after time, calling her to come and roost with him. Always he was greatly perturbed when she did not respond to what unquestionably was pleading on his part. However, though she was his mate, there was some unexplainable attraction, perhaps some inexplicable bond which we are not given to understand, that tied her to the human. Why not? We know there is often this bond between man and animal, a bond which seems to transcend that between this animal and another of his kind.

If I held Josie long enough she would tuck her head under her

80

Nearer

Almost there

feathers and go to sleep. She was so intent upon making my hand her sleeping-place that at times, if I entered when it was almost too dark to see, yet before she was asleep, she would leave Joey and her shelf and, with great difficulty in the gloom, find me. With the low, endearing notes with which she greeted her mate or he greeted her, she would climb until she reached my arm, along which she would creep until the open palm received her.

Her desire was not for warmth, for the observatory was well heated. The desire was for companionship.

Often I held her long, reluctant to disturb her contentment. But her ways and mine were foreign to each other, and although I do not doubt that she would have remained quietly in my hand all night, such could not be our way. When, with a disinclination as great as her own, I tried to return her to her partner she would cling to my fingers and crowd herself back into my hand, at the same time uttering low notes of protest.

At other times she seemed to want me to go to the shelf with her. Greeting me with those indescribably soft murmuring notes with which a bluebird greets a mate or another of their kind with whom they are on particularly friendly terms, she would run along my arm, creep into my hand and then fly to the perch. Repeated trips would be made from my hand or shoulder to the shelf where she would settle herself and adjust her wings in the manner of a bird moulding a nest. If I did not show any further attention she would then return to me. If, however, I placed my hand over her while she was on the shelf she would remain quiet and contented.

We are not apt to think of birds as having attributes similar to those of man, nor are we able to know of these until we gain the entire confidence of a bird. The birds in the wild do not and will not allow us to see into the innermost secrets of their minds. Not that we can see very far into the mind of a confiding bird, but at least they do not

81

attempt to keep their secrets from us. Once their trust is gained we may pry to our heart's content, have demonstrated to us their ways and their individual traits of character. Although we never may prove many of the things we think we learn, we might come closer to understanding than some persons would allow—if we read between the lines.

The bluebird is a graceful flyer

Little Blue and —

One more year passed. Now Josie had chosen her third mate, this time "Little Blue." After he was adopted from the garden bird house, Little Blue had been the shyest baby bluebird ever to take up residence in the observatory. Usually an hour or so of gentle coaxing will overcome the natural reluctance of a bluebird nestling to accept food—fear comes very early in life to *Sialia sialis* young ones—but this baby was *shy*. He was not stubborn nor was he more fearful than others of his kind. It took three days of coaxing to overcome this extreme shyness. Even when he accepted me as his foster parent and gave me his full confidence, he would crouch deep into his nest or into my hand if another person even entered the room. As the months passed, this shyness progressively lessened and by the time spring had come he accepted others of my kind as readily as he did me.

As nesting-time drew near, he and Josie were moved to the large nesting compartment in the summer octagon. These nesting compartments were eight in number, each facing in a different direction and forming, with the large flight in the center for non-nesting birds, an octagonal enclosure of considerable size. In the center flight were Josie's two sons and the other bluebirds, and other species.

When the nest-box was put in their compartment Josie and Little Blue became more excited than one unfamiliar with these birds could believe. Amidst exciting twittering and the waving of wings so peculiar to bluebirds it was examined time after time by both. With ecstatic voices interspersed with song from Little Blue they talked over its suitability. May we not infer a language? Birds have many more "notes"—vocal expressions—than those we usually hear in the wild. It is language, primitive as it may be, for it is understood by their kindred; and part of their language too is recognized by other songbirds. (Alarm notes uttered by a bluebird are instantly understood and acted upon by all the other species in the aviary, even by such exotic birds as the Asiatic Pekin robin, this too when warning actions are not observed.)

Various grasses were scattered by me on the ground and Josie lost no time in building her home. As soon as her nest was completed and her first egg laid, a little gate two by three inches with a shingle for a platform was opened in the mesh wire. Shortly afterwards both found this opening and learned again the joys of perfect freedom. Here was a situation built to order where an intimate study of the emotions of very expressive birds could be made. There were no handicaps for me except the lack of wings and, of course, the wall between birds and human beings. The first exception proved in the end almost as great a handicap as the second, for it limited the extent of my studies.

Five eggs were laid; five tiny nestlings hatched. I often wonder how Josie's one-year-old sons knew there were babies in that nest-box. Perhaps they knew both by the action of the parents and their audible expressions. Unquestionably they did know; for both yearlings began flying against the wire partition, clinging there and showing every evidence of excitement. Now developed, and intensified, a situation of which I had some hint during the winter. Little Blue, it had been noticed, often chased one of these brothers off a food dish, a perch or the bath; seemed to show a decided dislike for him and never allowed him to perch nearby. This never happened to the other. To him the greatest friendliness was shown, Little Blue even sitting or roosting close beside him. To roost beside him at night showed more than friendliness. There was some strong bond between them, unrelated as they were; for only if this were so would two birds of most species roost close together. No matter how friendly birds may be during the daytime, they usually resent the close proximity of another at night.

Now it was noticed that when the younger brother flew to the wire, Little Blue, if he was in the compartment, darted at him viciously until he left the wire. No attention was paid to the other when he tried to satisfy his curiosity. More than dislike was developing in Little Blue for the one—something which we know as "hate." This was forcibly brought to my attention the day after the last chick had hatched. Upon my entering his compartment to refill their bath, Little Blue flew over my shoulder and straight to the unloved one. Hurriedly I had to leave the compartment, separate the two little bundles of blue with my hand and carry Little Blue back to his home. There is no question of what would have happened had I not interfered. I know too well the fury which can possess these otherwise gentle birds. When this fury

84

has possession of them they have no mercy, and I am afraid no regrets. Shortly I was to see the opposite side of this picture and see it through tragedy.

If ever I saw gentle serene happiness among birds I saw it now. Saw it and absorbed it as I did the beauty of this early May. A small cloud on the horizon, "no bigger than a man's hand," perhaps made more poignant for me the gladness of these first few days. That small cloud took the form of a sharp-shinned hawk, a deadly and treacherous enemy. Rarely do these inveterate killers nest in our part of the province but seeing one at this time of year was a sure augury of a pair nesting within hunting distance. It would be exceedingly dangerous to allow Josie and Little Blue to secure food for their brood, yet to curtail their flights meant not only depriving them of their enthusiastic freedom, but it meant the loss of the little ones, for it was not within my power to supply them with the great quantities of insects needed for so young a brood. There seemed one solution, and even that fraught with danger. They could be allowed their liberty only when I could be in the garden with them. For the first few days that would mean spending most of the day from dawn to dark where I could watch. The catbirds, wood thrushes, evening and rose-breasted grosbeaks were also nesting and had liberty. Catbirds and thrushes were fairly safe, as they hunted for their food mostly on the ground, but the grosbeaks were in as much danger as the bluebirds, for their food was found among the trees.

The hunting ground of the bluebirds was in the flower garden and on the lawn. The grapevine posts and the tops of the unoccupied bird houses were their lookouts, although perhaps my shoulders were used almost as often. One cannot convey in writing the pleasure experi-

Bluebird alighting

enced as one or the other of these winsome birds came flying swiftly to alight and utter the same greeting as it would to its mate, the same salute with the waving wing. If it happened to be Little Blue, a gentle, yet pensive, warble was continuous while he lingered, intently watching the grass. Should Josie alight on my other shoulder there would be the same greeting and the same bewitching salute of the uplifted wing. I know of no other bird which greets another with the single wing (actually slowly waved), nor do I know of another greeting so lovely. The bluebird—greatly loved for his usual gentleness, the intenseness of his colouring ("the sky above and the earth beneath"), his welcome presence as the harbinger of spring, yes, even for the sad and pensive notes of his departure in the fall—engenders an even greater love when he is known, as he may be known, through birds like these.

Although Little Blue's song, while he was hunting food for his hungry brood, was the low mellow one so continuous all winter—not the more robust song of his courtship days—it seemed to be uttered musingly. His whole attention was on the grass, the soft brown eyes intent upon the slightest movement made by some unlucky insect. If the caterpillar he secured was a large one I was as apt as not to get well spattered with its green fluid as he hammered it on my shoulder. He knew I didn't mind, if he thought of it at all—I suppose we must presume he didn't.

A certain wonderment was present always when I watched them returning to the nest. Eight nesting compartments facing in eight different directions were inhabited by nesting pairs of various species. Each compartment was identical in shape and size, as was each gateway. Arbor vitae and spruce comprised the shrubbery. The partitions were of wire mesh through which the nest-box could be seen from any direction. The shortest way to the nest would seem to be through the entrance and compartment of some other bird. Many times they had to fly entirely around the observatory to reach their own, yet never were they confused. Even upon their first return they flew directly to their own gate.

Each year I wonder at this remarkable directional sense. Rarely have I seen any bird, other than the catbird, enter a compartment not its own. The male catbird in particular knew just why he was entering another. There were nests much too close to his own and there were eggs to break. Perhaps too some favourite food might be seen and some bird would at times enter to secure it for himself. Other than this, trespassing was rarely attempted. But how did they know?

Occasionally there was a temptation for me to open the door of the nest-box to see how the little ones were getting on. At times Josie would be warming them, but if so she merely looked up into my face. She did not object nor did Little Blue. Neither was there any resentment when I picked a baby out to measure its growth. The parents knew I was one who would not hurt their little ones. Why this confidence? It cannot be, I think, instinctive, for to birds man is an enemy. They have learned of course, but what is this learning? What thought processes go on in the tiny brain? Surely it must be reasoning of a kind. To me, to solve implies reason. Unquestionably their reasoning is limited, but to what extent we cannot determine exactly. Undoubtedly it varies greatly according to the species and also to some extent among individuals of the same species. Most certainly it does not seem to be absent, or limited, to the extent some would have us believe. Too many instances occur among trustful birds for them to be merely coincident.

Eleven days of exceeding anxiety passed. The two oldest in Josie's nest were now quite well feathered; the other three needed still the warmth of the mother at night, for many feathers had yet to develop. On the twelfth day, shortly after dawn, I went to the lower part of the garden and remained where I could watch the observatory and the bluebirds' hunting ground. As I arrived there Josie came and alighted on my shoulder for a few seconds and then—off to the lawn. Turning to watch Little Blue pounce on a beetle a short distance away I failed to notice where Josie went when she left the lawn. Several minutes passed and I saw Little Blue alone taking food to the nest.

Late that afternoon, while walking through the vegetable garden some hundred feet beyond the shrubbery which separated it from the lawn, I found the soft blue feathers scattered beside a marking stake, all that was left of Josie.

The tragic story was as plain as though I had seen it happen. Josie had alighted on a stake facing away from the nearby woods and was intently watching the ground. The sharp-shinned hawk had come from these woods like a bullet, and Josie never knew. These small hawks strike from ambush without warning and they are as treacherous as a weasel. Rarely do they strike in the open as do the more noble falcons, but fly through the woods at great speed to strike down the unsuspecting bird. I do not condemn them, much as I detest their tortuous ways, for like other predators they are but carrying out one of nature's methods of control.

There were five hungry, fast growing youngsters demanding more and more each hour with only Little Blue to supply their needs. That would be a big task for the father, perhaps an impossible task. I wondered if Josie's older son would help if I allowed him his freedom. He was now almost a year old and might seek a mate. However, I felt certain that he would not leave the vicinity, for this was his home and home meant the territory. Certainly Little Blue would not drive him away as he would the younger son. As I entered the observatory he was clinging to the wire partition watching the father enter the nest-box. I opened the door and called him to my hand. From there he flew to the nest-box where twittering greetings were exchanged with Little Blue; then he clung to the entrance, into which he thrust his head. What thoughts were in that little head just then—if there were thoughts? Was his tiny brain just a storehouse for instinctive reactions, or was there something more, something which we cannot measure?

At any rate he knew what he intended to do, conscious or unconscious of that knowledge, for as Little Blue flew to the gate he followed and began at once to seek food for his adopted family. I know, for I watched him; followed him and found that Little Blue had a willing helper, for he took back to the nest the very first insect he captured. There was no thought of a mate. There were babies to feed and even if they were not his own, that was his self-appointed task.

Early next morning I looked into the nest-box. Three still forms were lying on the bottom. Josie had not been there to warm the partially feathered ones and it is not the part of the male bluebird to brood the young. Here we see so plainly the limitations we must concede. The bluebirds belong to the family of thrushes and this family, brilliant in song, endearing in their ways, are not so adaptable as some of the others.

Now, until the two remaining ones were old enough to thrive on the food I could supply, I had to be more alert than ever. I chose a place where I could see the observatory and where I had a clear view of the entire territory where the bluebirds sought their food. I do not like to use a gun, but it would be best for the hawk not to strike again. Three times during the next few days I saw one fly over, but there was no further attack.

Little Blue and the older son of Josie and Jodee co-operated in perfect harmony during all the daylight hours. Under their care Josie's nestlings grew and prospered. As I worked in my garden nearby, both used my shoulders as listening posts, as had Josie and Little Blue, through the long days of early June. Then one day the two nestlings became fledglings; one brilliant blue, one dressed in the soft subdued colours that Josie had worn. After they left the nest I fed them often so that they would come to know and trust me. And they did. Another spring came and another nesting season when Little Blue must seek a mate to take Josie's place.

88

Bluebirds ready for a treat

For instance, would it not be strange to know that a bird could have an aversion to noise? I do not mean frightened by it. Noise, the cause of which is understood, is not frightening to them. No, I mean a bird may be irritated by it. There are many times when a hammer must be used in the observatory. I never remember using it that Josie did not object and show what appeared to be resentment. She did not always come to me when I entered; but if I started driving nails or hammering heavily, she would fly to me at once, uttering protesting notes. She would run back and forth on my arm; nestle in the hollow of my elbow; or even get on the hammer so that I would have to stop my work. When I ceased she would fly off, but as soon as I started hammering again she would come back and behave in the same way. Josie definitely objected in the only way she knew, and this not only in one instance but in many. Why, I do not know. No other bird in all the years had shown a like reaction. Could it be an idiosyncrasy?

When spring arrived she and Joey were given a nest-box. I scattered on the floor fine and coarse grasses like those used by bluebirds in building their nests. A nest was built and eggs were laid, but my unavoidable absence for three months precluded the possibility of their being successful with this home, for few understand the needs of native birds when they are nesting in confinement. When I returned late in the summer I went immediately to the observatory. Josie had not forgotten and greeted me, but would not nestle in my hand, much as I coaxed. However, when I entered again the next day, memory of her favourite place returned and she assumed her extraordinary display of fearlessness and manifestations of attachment.

We say that some species of birds mate for life. That is not strictly true. Some species do, however, remain mates for so long as each lives. Others may change mates each year or, as with the bluebirds, may remain mated for several years. Josie, although attached to me by a bond we do not fully understand and for as long as she lived, took a new mate each year. Little Blue was her third mate and her last, but curiously she left behind a son who helped finish her work.

Can They Replace — ?

Josie and her first mate Joey have taken the long journey and are with me no more. A new Josie and Joey have come, a sister and brother.

Joey II is more like the first Josie than any of the bluebirds I have come to know. Like her, he delights to rest on my hand after dusk has come, but I must not hold him close until the bedtime hour. Then I may close my fingers around him and stroke his head and back. He is more curious, more playful and mischievous than the first Josie. Instead of her dislike of noise and her protesting actions when I made it, he rides on the hammer when I am driving a nail, or tries to pull out the nail. Always the utmost care has to be taken not to hurt him, for he does not seem to know the meaning of fear except, of course, his instinctive fear of hawks. If I use a screwdriver he tries to balance himself on the round metal shank as it turns and at the same time pecks at the screw. If he is not up to tricks of this kind, then my lips, nose, or cheeks need pecking, or the lobes of my ears or my eyeglasses need investigating. When he tires of these he sees something on my clothes which should not, in his opinion, be there; or so it seems. There are large built-in cages on the wall for birds that get too pugnacious in the spring. The birds have access to these cages, if they are empty, and clean paper must be put on the bottom often. Young Joey has to help me with this paper in every cage. Here I am perplexed to know in what way he thinks he is helping me. Perhaps he thinks I am helping him, for at times, as I arrange the paper, he darts at my hand and pecks it as though in exasperation with my bungling ways.

The large bath is replenished often, but Joey knows a better place to bathe. The water in the pail is deep, too deep. He knows this, but that little head is not made of cotton: he knows where he wants to bathe, and he also knows there is a way. A hand held an inch under water makes a splendid bathing platform, and he soaks himself and me. Perhaps, though, the bath is filled first, and only an inch or two of water is left in the pail. No matter; dark as it is in the bottom, he waits. There is a hand he trusts, and he gets his way.

I rarely enter the storeroom at the end of the observatory without Joey riding on my shoulder. There are many things to investigate in there. Should I stand or sit quietly, however, he and his sister Josie creep along my arm and nestle together in the corner of my folded arms, or play about me. She is much like him, but has not his curiosity or his mischief. Perhaps, though, they are more alike than any other bluebirds I have known. So far there is a strong bond of affection between them, and I think this bond will continue even after each has taken a mate.

It is winter now, and dusk comes early. These two are somewhere on their favourite roosting shelf. Often I visit just before dark. Not a sound can be heard save the wings of a restless thrush. I call softly, "Joey, Josie." From the far end comes a plaintive note, then two shadows appear in the gloom. I open a little gate in the wire-covered doors. Right through the gate they come, and nestle close together in the corner of my folded arms. For a while they remain; then Josie grows restless, for it is getting dark and my arm is not her home. That home is her roosting shelf. Now ensues a pull between two desires. Both want to stay with me, yet both want to go home. Restlessness increases as first one and then the other hops on my fingers, then cuddles back in my arm. I do not coax them. At last the desire for home exerts the stronger pull, and they fly to the wire. Neither can find the gate in the increasing dark. I take them in my hand and show them the way.

As I reluctantly leave them, the soft murmuring notes of the blue-bird, crowding close to its mate on the roosting-shelf, gradually dies away. Stillness! Complete stillness and velvet dark.

92

The albino bronzed grackle must wait for his bath which has been pre-empted
by two mountain bluebirds (on ends of dish) and an Eastern red-breasted bluebird in back

Aye—She Was Bonnie

The year of the eighteen nestlings there seemed to be a scarcity of predators, and nests which would have ordinarily been destroyed by natural enemies were left unharmed. This meant that I had my pick of tiny subjects for the observatory. About the middle of May, I chose an eight-day-old bluebird from a nest in a garden bird house.

Her garden home had been deep and dark. The dimmed sounds of nature and soft twittering bird voices filtered through the small entrance above her head. Suddenly fear—panic! The twilight cave of the nest was gone. She was exposed and vulnerable. She could only crouch in apprehension and despair—homesick and lost.

Fiercely hungry, the nestling nevertheless refused to open her beautiful orange mouth for the food I offered. Gently, I held her in the cup of my hand. The food-stick, loaded with food, was slowly and persistently waved back and forth before her eyes. The insistent pangs of hunger gradually overcame fear. Shyly, tentatively, the little bill opened. Wider and wider it opened until a morsel of food could be placed deep within her throat. Shyness disappeared so quickly that it must have been swallowed with that food.

Now that the bluebird had accepted me as her parent, she began to accustom herself to the new world of the observatory. She soon became restless, not content to remain in the nest I prepared for her. And she was becoming aware: aware of intriguing new sounds and movements. One day she curiously followed the antics of a little fly on the windowpane beside her. She tried her little blue-grey wings and fluttered against the glass in an attempt to catch the insect. She missed the fly but the ties that had bound her to the nest were broken.

94

She explored her new quarters: not exclusively hers, as they contained guests of various species. She displayed a keen interest in inmates and surroundings alike and made friends wherever she went. Each day she grew more and more lovable and it became difficult for me to remain completely objective as I recorded my observations of the progress of this young member of the species *Sialia sialis*. She was developing her own personality traits. All of her characteristics were gentle. She never exhibited aggressiveness or hostility toward other birds in all the time she stayed with me. She had the unusual habit of looking directly into my face, and awarded me a trust that was touching.

The little bluebird enjoyed climbing about my person and once, after being fed, she hopped onto my hand, crouched down into the hollow of the palm and prepared to go to sleep. Her little greyish head was, for the first time, tucked under her wing in complete relaxation and trust. I sat for some time and wondered at the close contact established between this young bird and myself, reluctant to move lest I disturb that feathered slumber. I was still sitting with her in my hand when a visitor arrived and I was forced to change position to greet him. The bluebird wakened but did not take alarm, though up to this point I had been her only human contact. The stranger was accepted so readily that I became curious to how she would react if transferred to someone unfamiliar. Placed gently in the hand of the visitor, she crouched there as contentedly as she had in mine. This was a true test of the bird's tameness, because this person talked with his hands. He waved his arms as he emphasized one conversational point after another. I was becoming apprehensive that she might take fright and days of work might be undone. I need not have worried. The bluebird baby rode it out in a detached manner. Every now and then she cocked an eye to make sure she wasn't missing anything, but for the most part she slept. His hand was a cradle and she was content. Aye, she was indeed a bonnie baby! What else could we name her but "Bonnie"?

When Bonnie was nearly six weeks old she was quite able to help herself when she was hungry. We both knew this but each time I took up the food-stick (a piece of partly hollowed-out elderberry cane) she would open her bill wide for a tidbit. She enjoyed being babied and I could not resist indulging her.

About one month after Bonnie was adopted—about mid-June—the nursery was taxed by the addition of eighteen nestlings: three blue jays, three bobolinks, three cardinals, two Baltimore orioles, one cowbird, three wood thrushes and three veeries. (All, except the three blue jays, were together on a small, wire-mesh-enclosed porch, and these were the fifteen that Vee, the young wood thrush, later took on, fed so tirelessly—and mothered so charmingly.) None was more than ten days old and I had to start the seemingly never-ending task of feeding them. I prepared their food and Bonnie watched curiously while I dipped the food-stick into the food jar. She flew to my hand and waited expectantly. Its contents were given to another bird. A strange thing happened. She did not seem to be disappointed—just curious. She watched one nestling after another receive food which, until then, had been given to her. She was intensely interested. Something was definitely at work in that little head. Was it the awakening of parental feeling which appears to take place so early in the life of some bluebirds?

She watched the nestling feeding process several times before the food-stick was offered to her. She took the offering but, instead of enjoying it herself, kept it in her bill. Unexpectedly she turned to a tiny bird beside her and popped the food into its waiting mouth. It was obvious that I had an assistant. And with so many mouths to feed I surely needed one.

This was a strange turn of events. There were no birds with which she might identify, but Bonnie did not seem to care. It is exceedingly rare for a parent bird to feed the nestlings of another of its kind; still more rare to feed the product of another species altogether. Bonnie showed no favourites and adopted any little bird she could possibly mother. Her feeding programme was completely integrated and included any hungry mouth. She had taken on a fascinating task and that was all that seemed to matter to her.

Bonnie—can you see her? A baby still—her breast still vaguely spotted and still on nestling foods herself—hopping first to one young bird and then to another to give each its share of food? It seemed incredible but she was careful to see that each got no more than two helpings. If only one nestling was close by, Bonnie would feed it, then hunt up the next and then the next until all had been given their share. Sometimes she would forget her self-appointed role—to have a snack herself.

At first she took the nestlings' food from the food-stick I prepared. Later, noticing where the food came from, she perched on the edge of the food jar and took it directly from the container. I finally found a little more time to attend to other duties around the observatories.

This little bluebird helped out first with the group of eighteen nestlings, then with others, endearing herself especially to a pair of bluebird parents. She helped the mother, Josie, with every phase of her young ones' development until Josie's nest and babies had to be removed to the garden so that the parents could find the natural foods required to

96

raise very new nestlings. This event separated Bonnie from her adopted family. She would cling to the wire mesh of the observatory and coax me to let her out too. She was so disturbed, and coaxed so hard, that I overcame my feelings of mistrust and opened the door. At once she flew to the garden nest, looked in at the babies and then flew off to help with the feeding. She was happy now and I felt certain that she would remain within the garden area.

Shortly after noon of her first day outside I was watching these three care-free parents when what I felt sure were Bonnie's brothers and sisters came flying over the observatory. Apparently she had not forgotten them, for she called and joined them. Many, many times during the next few weeks when I saw bluebirds flying over I called "Bonnie, Bonnie"—for she had learned her name so well. The call of the wild was too strong. She was far away and she did not come back. I stopped waiting for her.

The seasons merged one into the other. The nestlings little Bonnie had helped to raise became amazing subjects themselves and kept me busy recording their behaviour patterns.

On a day almost two years after Bonnie left, on March the sixth, a near blizzard was raging. I happened to look out the kitchen window and there, in a sheltered winter feeding station a few feet away, was a female bluebird. How strange that she had come so early in the Ontario spring—alone, and in a storm.

I watched this little bird from time to time as she fed on the sumac berries: the only food available at this time of year. For almost two days I watched as she sought shelter in the feeder from the driving storm and bitter cold. She huddled against the March snow-wet wind and below-zero temperature. I wondered how she could possibly come through if the storm continued much longer and how I could help her to secure sufficient food.

I picked out a dozen mealworms from the breeding box and quietly approached her. Unbidden, a name I had not used for two years came to my mind. I called "Bonnie, Bonnie" as I threw a mealworm on the snow. Without hesitation she flew down and picked it up.

One at a time I threw down the others. The bluebird came to within a few feet of me, every now and then looking directly up into my face. Bluebirds are naturally shy of humans and this seeming tameness made me wonder. Could this possibly be Bonnie after nearly two long years? The garden bird house had not contained young birds the year before, and it is the habit of female birds to seek the territory of males. It seemed strange that this little female bluebird should remain here alone.

Juvenile European blackbird, albino robin and "Bonnie" Bluebird at the bath

The storm did not let up and I decided that the weather was not to take to itself this welcome little visitor. I knew that she could not survive exposed to the storm much longer. I secured a small cage, took the bottom off, placed a small dish with a number of mealworms in it under the cage, and raised one end of it slightly off the snow. At once she flew to it and went underneath. Gently the little lady was carried to the winter observatory and released among the other birds.

The visitor had no trouble adapting to the observatory. Ordinarily a wild bird is terribly frightened when introduced to unfamiliar objects. She showed no fear of the food cups, of the bathing dish or of the other birds. She appeared to be at home with them. Later, she came to my hand for her favourite food. Surely this must have been Bonnie home again. Of course I called her "Bonnie."

The blizzard wore itself out and soft warm spring days, melting snow and budding trees brought back our summer birds: the robins, the bluebirds, the song sparrows and, as the days lengthened, many others. By the end of April the removable sashes were taken off the windows of the cottage. Bonnie and all those who had not known the

98

warmth of the direct sun and the fresh outdoors for six long months now revelled on the damp earth and in the soft southerly breezes. They flew and climbed and basked in that indefinable something that always comes with spring! That ineffable mixture of nostalgia, sweet sadness, mystic renewal and inexpressible wonder that comes to us all. And with the spring too, a rondeau from the throats of native birds: the clear, sweet whistles of the cardinals and the merulas (European blackbirds) mingling with the flute-like notes of the wood thrushes, the liquid cadences of the veeries and the unutterably delicate court-ship songs of the rose-breasted grosbeaks and the soft, gurgling warble of the bluebirds.

The sixty-foot-long flyway from the cottage to the summer and breeding quarters did not seem new to Bonnie as it did to some of the others. She flew back and forth as though it were a well-remembered route. Nor did she cling against the enclosing wire mesh trying to get out, as a bird unused to being enclosed would do. Yet, tame as she was, never in the many years after she returned to me did she trust me as she had before. Long memories seem to be the rule among most songbirds, and the long separation did not dull the memory of her early home and foster parent. It did, however, revive the mistrust of humankind inherent in these birds. Bonnie was a very young bird when she left the observatory and it was remarkable that she gave me her trust at all, even with certain reservations.

A number of male bluebirds were with Bonnie, yet in all the years she remained with me she never took a mate. It was not that she was not courted, for she was. She had a great deal of appeal for the eligible bachelors in the observatory and she sang her soft warbling siren song as female bluebirds do, although not so often in later years; for blue-birds begin to age at eight and are old at ten. Bonnie reserved her affection for me and for the nestlings of others.

From a strictly technical point of view this little subject provided my research with a wealth of valuable material. She was with me so long, though, that a personal understanding developed between us. We had become close friends and when she finally left me altogether I missed her sorely.

I often think of Bonnie and the interpersonal relationships she had with other birds in the observatory. They must have missed her too.

From a Far-off Place

Why did Bonnie Bluebird give back to me the raisin I had given to him? I had been watching Bonnie—but let us go back through the years.

A cicada is singing, high up in the locust tree: the only sound in that stillness of dancing heat waves. In the shade of the locust, lying in the gently swaying hammock, is one who is drowsily wondering. Wondering why only the cicada seems to enjoy such heat. It is too hot to wonder—let it sing. The slightly swaying hammock comes to rest, and just as deeper drowsiness takes over there drifts across the lawn a new note: the gentle, plaintive call of the bluebird. She listens—there is something different about that note! The bluebird house in the garden is not so far away and now she can see the reason for the different call. It is nearly time, it would seem, for the little ones to leave their dark home.

As she watches, this lover of birds sees the father on a branch with a caterpillar in his bill; can hear his coaxing calls to his young to come out. There too, in the entrance, she can just make out the head of a nestling bluebird as it peers at the strange world outside. The father keeps calling and coaxing, but his eldest is not quite ready for the first adventurous flight. The little head stretches far out, then ducks back out of sight only to appear again in a moment. Undoubtedly the father knows it is time for his brood to come forth, for instead of flying to the nest and giving the worm to the soon-to-be fledgling, he eats it himself. The little fellow must learn that if he is to eat he must fly to his parents instead of having father and mother bring food to him.

Now the pity of it is that these five hungry babes have, with their parents, consumed most of the insects close to their home. Farther afield the parents must range to secure what they need, and that farther

100

afield means under the trees on the side of the road where caterpillars drop from the leaves. It is a dangerous place to seek food, for motor cars speed past in July. Often, lately, the father has sought their food there and probably has had many narrow escapes. Perhaps in his desire to hurry them from their nest he was not as alert as he might otherwise have been, or maybe the car was going at a very high speed. Whatever the reason, the little fellow with his head in the entrance will never again be coaxed to come out by his brilliant blue father.

What a task is left for the mother! Five big hungry youngsters, just ready to leave! Now she alone must find tempting bait that will induce these five to leave their babyhood home, all the necessary food until they grow old enough to find it themselves; the only one to warn them of dangers in the great world outside.

Another day must come before the eldest, now grown bolder, more restive for the new world to be seen from the entrance, is ready to leave. A little more coaxing by his mother and he is in a nearby tree. Then another head appears in the entrance, and he too is free; then another and another, each one hesitating for a moment, then off to the trees. Each alights a little way from the others for they must not be together if danger comes near.

The last little head appears, remains looking for long, but seemingly cannot get up courage to launch into the air. The mother bird coaxes; feeds her other fledglings, and coaxes again and again, but he will not leave. Like all parent birds, the mother wants to lead her family away from the nest, partly, perhaps, because she knows from some inner urge that they are vulnerable there, partly because she must seek farther afield if she is to feed well her large family. Every time she calls she seems to be farther away. At last the little fellow, seeing his mother, his brothers and sisters, now so far off, tries his wings. But, instead of reaching a tree, he falls to the ground.

Now, it would seem, this little one needs a friend, and that friend *must* be one of our humankind. This friend is at hand. To see the mother and her four going farther and farther away; to see this youngest of the five apparently not yet quite old enough, not yet strong enough to fly and keep up with the rest, creates a feeling of anxiety. Perhaps more, it creates a feeling of frustration difficult to describe. The thought comes that if she puts the youngster on a high branch he might be able to take off, gain strength as he attempts to fly, and be able to join all the others.

Running to where the little bird is down in the grass, she lifts him and places him high on a branch. That will not do. Try as he does, he is unable to fly from one tree to another. Fond of birds as she is—

feeding them in winter, putting up nesting houses for them in the spring as she has done for so long—she never has reared a nestling by hand. Yet she must take care of him and she does.

Off in the distance she can hear the mother bird call. She is far away. She is not coming back! But she does come back. She has not forgotten her youngest, for when it is placed on a branch she calls with coaxing, enticing notes and tries so hard to induce the little fellow to follow her. He tries, but each time falls to the ground. For three days the mother often returns, leaving her family on the new feeding grounds. Not until late in the third day do his wings become strong enough to hold him up in the air.

On the morning of the fourth day, when the mother arrives, the little fellow is placed high on a branch of a tree. Again she tries so hard to coax him to follow her; sits close to him; hops a little way off and then back; then flies off with inviting calls which become louder and more urgent. He will not follow. There is another who has become his father-and-mother and he is staying with her. For an hour he is left on the branch in the hope that he will change his mind. But when he begins to droop in the hot summer sun a finger is placed under his breast; a little hop to the finger and he is ready to ride.

Now there is only one thing to do: take the little one into the house and continue the search for insects to feed him—and hope for the best. A small wicker covered basket is prepared for a nest. Then begins again the hunt which must be kept up day in and day out, for the crickets, grasshoppers and caterpillars so essential if he is to live. Many moths too are captured under the lights in the evening, but these last only part of the day. What a task it becomes! Only the essentials of housework can be allowed to interfere with the seemingly never-ending hunt for live food for this little orange mouth. Does this seem like carrying love for a bluebird too far? This lovable mite who creeps into her hand for his sleep or cuddles close to her neck, who coaxes with waving wing for the food that will keep him alive—he must live.

He does live and he grows, and each day he endears himself more. As evening approaches after a very hot day he begins to get cross as a child that is overtired; will scold as each evening she puts him to bed in the little wicker basket where he utters his low, sweet warble—a song that sounds like wheels going over hard snow, a song that lasts for moments then grows into silence as sleep overcomes him.

At last, after more than two weeks of exacting care and anxiety— the danger of accident in the house is ever present—the burden of keeping the little fellow supplied with insect and berry food becomes so difficult that some decision must be made about his future. To keep

102

him in a cage is unthinkable; to allow him the run of the house impossible, for the two Persian cats cannot be kept in the basement much longer. Yet, to give him his liberty means almost certain early death, for he has no fear of cars or cats or people. Yes, there are people who can be almost as dangerous to birds as are cats.

The bird lover, Jenny Alsdorf of Wallkill, New York, had read of my Bonnie, had named her own little waif Bonnie too; so she wrote asking me what was best. Here among those of his kind he would be happy (if I am right in thinking a bird can be happy, which some with ice in their veins will deny). Full circumstances were explained to the Fish and Wildlife Service in Washington and a permit was issued which allowed Bonnie to be given to me. It was necessary also, however, to acquire a similar permit from the state in which Bonnie was born. This permit was curtly refused. The reason? According to the official who had charge of issuing such permits, our bird lover had broken the law which protects birds. In his eyes it was a crime on her part to have saved the life of the little bluebird. She was informed that she ought either to have left little Bonnie to die, or to have seen, herself, that he died, rather than break the law; that a game warden would call immediately, seize the bird and release it.

Now here is where Bonnie "took over." The officer called with his orders and Bonnie proceeded to show him why he could make a mistake. His badge of office needed quite close inspection, and both his hair and the lobe of his ear needed pulling. In no time at all Bonnie entered the heart of this officer: entered into it so deeply he said: "Take your Bonnie to Canada; take him right away, and I shall explain to the higher authorities in full why he must not be given his liberty."

Could he be sent by express? No, he was too precious to be trusted to strangers. Our bird lover and her husband drove four hundred and sixty-five miles to bring Bonnie to me. Can you wonder at the letter she later received from far away British Columbia, in which the writer said, after having read in a national magazine the story of this little bird: "When I read about you and your little bluebird I thought how nice to be able to afford a thousand-mile trip on account of a little bird. And then I saw quite clearly that you will always be enormously rich—even without a cent to your name."

That letter did not, however, express the sentiments of the state authority. When our bird lovers arrived home, after their thousand-mile drive, there awaited another officer sent by the state—to seize Bonnie. He was too late.

Little Blue the bluebird and a cedar waxwing

Bonnie loved everyone, but, there is no doubt in my mind that the one he knew from earliest days was missed for a time at least. The morning after he came to me, as I was holding him in my open palm, his lady arrived to bid him goodbye. At once he left me to fly to her shoulder. Although he would not yet open his bill for me, the moment she spoke the little bill opened for the food he knew he would get from her. Soon, though, he learned what the food-stick meant; learned to like his new food; learned that I could, and would for a time, take the place of his foster mother. He became completely at home. But, strangely, he would have nothing to do with the other bluebirds.

104

Now there are times when a cage is his home for an hour, for sometimes there is work to be done that cannot be done if Bonnie is free. Like the second Joey he must help with everything that I do, and should it happen that I forget for a fraction of some second—! Yet, by being exceedingly careful, often I can let him satisfy his intense interest in all that I do. If I am doing lighter work, such as tacking up weatherstrip in the fall before winter windows are put on, then he may have his fun. But I have to hold him while I drive a tack. Otherwise he would pull the tack before I had a chance to drive it home, or a much more serious something might happen—to that little head. Then when the tack is driven he does his best to pull off the weatherstrip. In all that I do he delays my work so much, yet I cannot bring myself to withhold him from his playful pranks.

Sometimes I wonder if what we call jealousy is not one of his traits; for, should a bird (even a much larger one such as a grosbeak) alight on my shoulder, Bonnie junior, if he is near, is almost sure to drive him off. First he stares and opens his bill, then, in a sudden swoop, rising high and in fury, drops on its back. Courage also he has in plenty, more courage than I have ever seen in any other bluebird. A rose-breast, or cardinal, or robin may be feeding from a dish. Should Bonnie take a notion that he wants that particular food, without hesitation he dives with such sudden force that the bird does not stay to dispute his right. He will not strike a jay. But should he be in the bath, and a blue jay have the same desire, Bonnie will crouch in the water, open his yellow mouth, and dare the jay to put him out.

Spring is not so far away, and Bonnie—well, maybe there will be trouble then. There are three female bluebirds from which to choose; or perhaps only two, for I think that already Little Blue and his last year's mate have paired again, and, although *I* am now Bonnie's "mate," when the urge to nest becomes strong he will choose from among his own. Perhaps he will choose female Bonnie, although she is now getting old. But whichever one he does choose, I am afraid he will brook no rivals, and that is sure to mean serious trouble.

I can only wait and watch—and let him hunt me up to feed me some favourite food, perhaps a dearly loved raisin he thinks I need, even though he has to give it to me through the wire mesh.

A Year Has Passed

Later in that approaching spring in which I expected trouble between Bonnie junior and Little Blue, trouble did come. Little Blue did pair again with the third Josie. Bonnie junior showed no desire to mate with either old female Bonnie or one-year-old Beebee, but that did not prevent his being intensely jealous of Little Blue and Little Blue returned this feeling in full. Often I had to pull apart these little bundles of fury, then had to keep them separate until Bonnie could be put into the summer observatory, in early May. Had I not separated them, either Bonnie or Little Blue might have lost more than their brilliant blue feathers.

In young Bonnie's summer home were bluebird nest boxes in which he was intensely interested, but most decidedly he was not interested in females of his kind. He wanted a nest built—if I would build it. To me, and not to one of them, he brought his favourite worm or raisin. One might have thought this attachment to me, inexplicable as it was, would have ended when nesting season was over, but not at all. All summer long I was the one to whom he brought his favours.

And now, spring is again not so far away. As Bonnie has been doing all fall and winter, he still brings to me the dearly loved treat. I must have the first he gets. The second usually belongs to him. If it is a mealworm, he hammers it until it is, in his estimation, in fit condition for me; or if it is a raisin, it too must be made soft and broken. Holding this treat in his bill he flies around the observatory hunting me and calling with the peculiar call a bluebird uses when he informs his mate or young that he has a treat for them. Amazing little bird! His behaviour is beyond all understanding. With the exception of the first Josie, never before have I known a bird so persistent in his attentions to man. Even the first Josie was different from Bonnie, for it was *my* attention to *her* that *she* craved.

But being an amazing little bird does not help his temper where eight-year-old Little Blue is concerned. Mild spats have been frequent all winter, neither one being able to dominate the other, but now that spring is so close and nesting time draws near, these little quarrels have been getting more serious.

This very day a furious battle raged while I watched, and Bonnie came off the victor. No damage was done, for as soon as Little Blue found himself mastered he flew to my shoulder. This however did not save him, for Bonnie at once knocked him off. Little Blue flew to the far end with Bonnie a scant foot behind, and straight back to me. This time he alighted under my chin and as I put my hand up he crept into the palm. I have heard of birds flying to human beings for safety, have hesitated to accept such statements as facts; but now I had proof. To quiet his fast-beating heart I took him into the house, carried him from room to room for a while, at the same time stroking his blue head and back. He was content. Usually when a bird is mastered, its fear is so great that blind instinct rules, and it tries to hide in some inconspicuous place. Why did Little Blue come to me twice for protection instead of following the general pattern—to hide? Was it instinctive reaction to terror, or was there some semblance of thought as to where real safety lay?

Most songbirds are exceedingly fond of raisins and Bonnie was no exception. Also—my abject apologies to those to whom so-called anthropomorphic expressions are anathema—he became very fond of me. So fond of me that I had to have the first two or three treats before he would swallow one himself. Giving these treats to me was, for the

A frightened orphan

present, not necessarily a sign of fondness. Fledgling bluebirds often help their parents by feeding their second brood, and perhaps to Bonnie I was just another bluebird that needed food. Yet that does not seem to explain entirely his behaviour towards me, for not only did he continue all winter to give me his treats but, in the following spring, he refused to mate with any one of the several bluebirds I had here. I was his mate—another bluebird? I must build a nest. What excitement as he lifted one blue wing in salute! What sweet and coaxing warbling as I lifted the lid of a bluebird house and put grass inside! This also is not too unusual. It is not unknown for a hand-reared bird to behave towards the one who has reared it as it would to one of its own kind.

But Bonnie was a different bird from any I had known or heard of before. Not that being different is unusual in itself, for no two birds are alike in characteristics even when from the same nest. Perhaps I should say that he was *very* different. Although he rarely gave his treats to me during his second winter, he began to do so when the next spring arrived. But here followed a puzzle I have not yet been able to solve, if it is solvable.

Beebee was one of the female bluebirds and a former mate of Little Blue. This second spring she chose Bonnie for her mate, and he gave me up—as his mate. But, apparently, not as his valued friend. I, however, took second place—up to a point. When I gave him a treat he gave it to Beebee; gave her a second and a third; but no matter how she coaxed for more, I had to have the fourth and fifth and sometimes the sixth. Then the next two or three were his.

These treats were for us only, not for any other—until his little light blue eggs turned into tiny chicks. Then I, like Beebee, was left out. Yet occasionally he would share with me. But there were too many hungry mouths to feed for him to be too generous. Too many caterpillars to be sought among the trees and shrubbery where he and Beebee sought all the live food so necessary for their five tiny nestlings.

The next late winter and early spring, and the next and the next for eight long years, Bonnie brought his treats to me and, when mating time came, to his partner of that season. Bonnie and Little Blue are now with the years that have gone: both were old birds—Bonnie went in his tenth year and Little Blue in his fifteenth. But I shall never forget, so long as memory serves, the friendship, the affection, of this little waif from a far-off place.

108

Scarlet tanager

Steller's jay

A communal feast

Twelve-day-old blue jays

Other Things to Tell

There is much more that could be told of Josie and Joey and Little Blue and their—and my—companions who have resided with me throughout the years; who have, because of their lovable natures, their beauty, their quaint and entrancing ways—yes, even their perverse and difficult ways—endeared themselves beyond normal comprehension. But there are other things too to tell. What has gone before are incidents—incidents giving us an insight by which we may unravel at least a part of the mystery of their lives. Such unravelling of what seems to be a tangled skein has been the endeavour of many, and these many are divided among several classes of thought. We have the so-called "mechanist," the cold-blooded, unimaginative and somewhat cruel scientist who sees Josie as a mere living mechanism without initiative, without motive or endeavour other than that derived from some fixed law which controls all her impulses: in other words, she could be explained in terms of physics and chemistry.

On the other hand there are those who, from pure sentimentality, give the birds a place in nature almost equal to themselves. This outlook on the lives of birds is unwarranted and, beneath the surface, is due to excessive feeling and lack of thought. Oversentimentality is not an aid in measuring and analyzing the behaviour of birds so that we may determine whether their conduct is a thing apart—or akin to that of man, varying in degree only. In between these extremes are other persons who in their thinking do not dig deep. They fail to read nature's open book; they call such deductions as mine "anthropomorphic," in a derogatory sense; which does not help to solve the problem of kinship.

I have not, in all I put before you, departed from observations of my own covering a period of forty years. These observations have been

This glass feeder, upon pressure of the plunger,
exudes a worm-like thread of nestling food

largely of native birds that I have fostered and cared for; many of them
I have reared by hand. It has been said the reason for this is that "the
bird in the wild does not show its true personality. This personality
we find in a hand-reared bird because it acts towards the one who rears
it as it would towards its own family. In no other way can we get onto
a bird's own level."

To this I would add that often the hand-reared bird, in its behaviour
to the one who rears it, advances beyond the relationship with its own
family and acquires a personality mysterious and perhaps imponder-
able. In fostering these birds I have tried to give them an environment
as close as possible to that of nature. They are never kept in cages unless
they are ill, injured, or are inclined to be dangerous to others of their
company during certain seasons. The studies I have made are based
upon an intimacy which can be gained only by virtually living with
them; my suggestions and sometimes my conclusions are based upon
these studies.

To become intimate with birds requires close association, not only
physically but also mentally. As no two birds are alike in disposition,
we must differentiate between them by separating them in our minds.
I have found that when a bird is given a name, then it takes on a personality; becomes an individual—a clear-cut image in the observer's
mind. This individualization leads to closer study because of increased
interest: we do not now study only the machine which is a bird, we
study a living entity. Interest in that individual must be intense so that
we may probe deep. Thus the naming of a bird is not "romantic folly,"
but an aid in gaining knowledge. So that in your mind each bird may
come to life, I have made use of names.

110

Such Curious Behaviour

The way of a bird is often peculiar and, more than peculiar, sometimes mysterious. Much of their behaviour is routine. Nature forms a pattern and the pattern controls a large part of their lives. The more obvious moulds such as nesting, breeding, and rearing their young we can readily understand. Also we begin to see, not dimly, the reason they sing, choose home sites and protect these from their kin. But there are other forms of behaviour for which we seem to find no real explanation—behaviour so curious, seemingly so without reason, that all our ingenuity has not yet unravelled the puzzle.

One of these has been given the somewhat curious and perhaps inexact name of "anting." By this is meant that an ant is picked up by a bird and rubbed on some part of the plumage (on the ventral surface of the wing or tail), then usually eaten. At first glance there seems nothing so remarkable about this, although we may wonder why the ant is rubbed under the wings before it is eaten. Of course, after all, the answer seems simple. The ant secretes acid. When it is seized by the bird, most likely the acid is expelled by the ant. To prevent swallowing too much, the secretion is rubbed off on the feathers.

But wait! There are birds that swallow the ant without rubbing it first. And such birds are so closely related to birds which do scour the feathers that our first interpretation seems flawed. Then why do they do it? Several explanations—mere theories—have been advanced by scientists and others who have seen the performance in various parts of the world. Have you seen it? If so, you are one of the fortunate, for few students of birds have ever seen a bird anting. Perhaps not more than a comparative handful in all the world have seen this strange, amazing and amusing performance.

111

Blue jay rubbing ant on underside of third primary

Many times of late years I have spread a shovelful of earth from an anthill before all the birds. Late in the fall, in winter, and in early spring not a great deal of interest is shown. But in May, June or July there is often a rush to the ant-filled earth by most of the birds. As we watch them we can hardly believe what we see. Their antics are comic and clownish and charming. The tail is drawn forward, often under their feet; one wing also is drawn forward, far forward and up; then with a swift sidewise motion the ant, in one single stroke, is rubbed down towards the end of a feather.

If the tail is far to the front and the feet stand upon it, then the bird is in for a tumble—right on its back. Can you see Sherr, the old rose-breasted grosbeak, with rose on his breast and rich salmon under his wings, as he falls backwards, displaying his beauty in full? Yet that very tumble, so unlike what one expects of a bird, is so comical that tears of laughter may spring to the eyes. The whole anting performance is not only remarkable, but is a beautiful and fascinating circus to see.

Copious notes have been taken in the songbird observatory, still pictures have been made, and fast and slow motion pictures in black and white and in colour, to try to determine why some birds ant and

112

why others, related, do not. Perhaps twenty-five birds will ant all at once on a space only three feet by three. But to see just what they do and where ants are rubbed, one only must be watched at a time. The action is rapid, so rapid indeed that the eye is usually unable to follow their movements accurately. The anting of Scarlet the tanager and Ori the Baltimore oriole is somewhat slower than that of the others, and I follow their movements with care. After hundreds of viewings I have found that the ant is rubbed only on the underside of the outer flight feathers and, but more rarely, on the underside of the tail. Not once in years of close study have I seen the ant rubbed on any other part of the plumage.

Then why do they ant? One student will interpret their actions as a method of ridding themselves of parasites, internal and external. Another, as dressing their feathers for the agreeable effect of the acid. There are many more guesses and theories, any one of which may seem tenable—until we dig deep. Perhaps all of these theories are based upon casual observation of a spectacle unexpectedly presented. What seems to be seen is not really seen. The bird is not dressing its feathers with ants indiscriminately, as most observers believe; although in rare instances this, I am told, has been seen. So far as songbirds are concerned (I am not including the crow), in my experience they do not rub the ants on the feathers of any part of the body except under the wing and under the tail. When they do use the ant in this way, it is not *placed* under the wing, but *rubbed* near the tip of an outer wing feather and on the ventral surface of this feather. It is then discarded or eaten. A bird may pick up a fresh ant a hundred or more times and each time the action is apparently identical. This fact alone seems to dispose of many theories as to why a bird ants. But there is more. A robin will ant and a bluebird will not. Both eat ants. Yet these two birds are believed to be closely related. Their requirements in almost all ways are the same. Can you think of a reason why the robin should ant and the bluebird should not? Or can you think of any plausible explanation of why so many species do ant?

Although I have seen this extraordinary performance so often—so many hundreds of times—I cannot advance even a reasonable theory. Were it not for the two facts presented above, perhaps we could solve it. But do these not seem like "stone walls"?

Our understanding is less dim when we observe another peculiarity of birds, one perhaps not so peculiar after all when we consider how much we too like the sun. At times during the heat of summer a visitor will point out a bird lying on its side, its mouth wide open and feathers

113

fluffed, and want to know if this bird is sick. To those, and there are many, who have not before seen a bird taking a sun bath, the position assumed seems so entirely unnatural that the thought of illness comes instantly to mind. Not only is our bird far from being ill, it is, we believe, insuring itself against illness.

If you have not seen the performance, examine with care the.picture of Sherr, the old rose-breasted grosbeak, as he yields to his love of the sun. This photograph was taken in the great heat of summer and his wing was not fully expanded as it might have been had the heat rays not been so intense. Usually, if the heat is intense he will face away from the sun, as this picture will show. His bill is wide open, his head is turned sideways so that the rays enter his mouth, while one eye gazes directly at the sun. The feathers of his crown are nearly erect while those of the body are so fluffed that the rays must penetrate to the skin. One wing is partly, and the tail fully, expanded and the feathers of his rump are erected so high that the oil gland receives a full share of the rays of the sun.

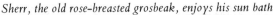

Sherr, the old rose-breasted grosbeak, enjoys his sun bath

A sun-bathing catbird

This posture is assumed by most of our songbirds when sun-bathing. But some, like the bluebird, lie flat on their breast with both wings spread outward and forward to the fullest extent. Some too, like the catbirds, may take either position, depending apparently on whim. A few species, when sun-bathing, hold one wing extended and high so that the rays reach the flank. This position, however, is not often seen.

When the sky is clear blue, the air still, the sun beating down in full force, then is the time to watch songbirds taking their sun baths. Not only are these baths taken more often on clear days, but for a much longer time. Sun-bathing during such days is often so prevalent that it seems to be the dominant part of their lives.

Why do they bathe? Certainly not to get tanned. It must be that nature, using the rays of the sun, produces some chemical reaction essential to the absorption of food. Some believe that through irradiation a vitamin is stored in the feathers and that, in preening, a bird in some unknown way ingests a vitamin necessary to health. Others believe that the rays of the sun perform this function by way of the skin. Whether either or neither is right, nature shows us some remarkably beautiful pictures as we watch sun-bathing birds.

Should We Compare?

Authority* states: "It is almost impossible to avoid comparing birds with mankind . . . but any serious effort at comparison is absurd." Is it *almost* impossible, or *impossible*? Why avoid such comparison? Man's superiority over birds, except in the realm of the spiritual and the intellectual, seems to be measured only by degree, and as the eminent naturalist Hugh M. Halliday has said: "To take apart the mentality of any other creature we must turn to the workings of our own mind. When we view the actions of any one of the so-called lower animals we see them from the standpoint of human experience." Have we any other measure?

Again authority states: "To endow birds with human traits is tantamount to implying as a premise that one class of vertebrates can really bear comparison with a higher class."

The above is the equivalent of a definite presumption, or statement of fact. But what proof is there that man is the only creature on earth to possess powers of emotion that cannot be approached remotely by any other creature? In fact, what *right* has man to presume he has a monopoly of such emotions? We who wish to learn the truth desire a statement of fact to be based upon a firm foundation. To deny rather than to know is a failing in human nature. How does anyone *know* that human and bird traits have nothing in common?

It is true that our interpretation of emotions—such as fear—cannot be shown to be correct except by inference, and that we are greatly handicapped in interpreting them because birds cannot answer questions. However only in the exact sciences can we have absolute proof. If a man were unable to answer questions we would be handicapped in investigating his sense of smell, but his inability to answer would not be proof that the sense of smell was absent. If we can show only by

*I use the designation "authority" (here and elsewhere) to represent professional ornithologists and biologists in general.

116

inference that a bird has an emotion of fear, that is not proof that the emotion is absent.

The premise that the emotion of fear is not comparable to the same emotion in man is undemonstrable. (Here I am not speaking of degree or relative importance.) The most that we can say is that, as far as we can observe, fear is evanescent. That it is of a different quality, less intense, less enervating in bird than in man, seems to be not only unprovable—experiment would seem to prove the opposite.

Early in May of a year gone by, when Sherr the rose-breasted grosbeak was young and his kind were on their northern migration, I hung a cage in a tree. In this cage I placed Sherr, who now needed a mate, in the hope that he would attract one of the migrating females. An inquisitive catbird entered one part of the cage and was trapped. As I approached to release this prying bird it went into a panic of fear. When I opened the door of the cage it fluttered out and fell to the ground, where, paralyzed with fright, it struggled for a moment and then dashed into the side of the observatory. Here was shown a loss of all co-ordination induced by extreme fear. Such fear seems to be, by inference, identical with that which can paralyze the human brain under similar circumstances.

Had I taken the catbird in my hand it might have died. Had it done so and a post-mortem been made, it is probable that the physiological cause of death would have been found to be cerebral hemorrhage. The hemorrhage could be *proved* by dissection. The cause of the hemorrhage could be *proved* in bird or man only by inference. (Here I am speaking of fear only.) If we accept it as proof in the case of a man, to be logical it seems to me that we should accept it in the case of a bird.

Fear which we may designate as simply alarm has many causes and is transient. It is rightly said that there is no evidence of a feeling of suspense in birds; that their lives are not clouded by it. However, genuine fear as a human being can feel it may be felt by a bird, as illustrated by the catbird. The shortness of duration does not alter the fact that it is present. All species may not react to fear to the same degree. A hawk may strike terror into a flight of warblers by attacking and killing one, and this terror may abate even while the hawk is devouring their companion in full view. A passing bird hawk, such as a Cooper or sharp-shinned (not the large circling *Buteo*) will induce bluebirds to give, first, the alert and then, if close, the alarm note; a striking hawk will induce the same birds to "freeze" for many minutes, or long after the hawk has passed from sight.

You will remember that when Rajah the golden eagle was brought to me it was necessary to give him careful and painful treatment which

117

lasted for five months; that during the first half of this period his whole body trembled while the wound was being cleaned. This trembling was caused by pain. How do I know it was caused by pain when he could not tell me so? In his case there could have been two causes only for trembling: pain or fear. Simple deductions from actions would seem to be ample proof. At no time during the year I took care of him before release did he show fear of me, when I went near, by either attack or retreat, or by trembling. Concrete proof of this is that for the first few months, unable to tear his own food, he took it from my fingers. That this bird was capable of fear was, however, distinctly evident. When I entered carrying a stick he showed by precipitate retreat that, in so far as we could determine, this object was associated in his mind with a gun. You will recall that during the early stages of his treatment it was necessary at times to carry him. Gauntlets were used on such occasions. During the latter part of his convalescence (some seven months), if I entered wearing gauntlets or carrying them in my hand, he showed definite signs of fear of these, as he had of the stick. His memory here was of obnoxious imprisonment in my arms, and the gauntlets were associated in his mind with such imprisonment.

Would it not seem that this demonstration of fear was analogous to the fear exhibited by an arrested man who trembled violently when handcuffs were about to be placed on him? This comparison leads to the question of motive. Was the inciting cause dissimilar in the two cases? I suggest, it was not. Consciousness of possible imprisonment, with its loss of liberty, was present in both. What is left then is the question of degree. This question we cannot answer, nor is it of present consequence.

Here we have evidence that one emotion, fear, is comparable in man and bird. If it can be demonstrated that one emotion in a bird can be compared to the same emotion in a man, then it is illogical to contend that other emotions cannot be compared. I can find no evidence which *proves* that fear or any other emotion in the bird is not comparable to the same emotion in man.

In the wild state among many birds, confidence, the opposite of fear, is not a characteristic. Nature has endowed birds, for some good reason, with supreme selfishness. As we all know selfishness does not breed confidence. Consequently, except among some species and during the breeding season, each bird to a greater or lesser degree is alert for any onset by its companions.

Partial or complete confidence in a human being, however, may be learned by a bird. Such confidence is shown by Ori, the Baltimore oriole who has been with me for several years. When he came to me

118

An oriole accepts a treat from a friend

he was young and wild. Slowly confidence developed until there came a time when he was ready for the friendship test. Leaning far forward from a branch he suddenly whacked me hard upon the thumb with that needle-like bill of his, then after a momentary pause gently took a peanut from between my fingers. Unlike most birds that make this test, Ori was not yet sure of me and for several days rapped me hard each time I offered him a treat. At last he was convinced that he could trust me and he has never struck me since. How like our human-kind! Not always is our confidence easily gained. Can you in truth tell me that Ori's established confidence is not comparable to the confidence engendered between man and man through mutual trust?

119

No Perspicacity?

It seems to me that in trying to determine the ways of birds we should try to be specific. Authority* states: "There is remarkably little outside the standard pattern of behaviour for any given species. There would appear to be little free will or choice in conduct. In spite of this extremely limited range of capacity there is some individual variation in capacity, as well as considerable specific variation."

To me there seems to be a contradiction here. Perhaps the word "behaviour" is used in too broad a sense. Behaviour, based upon what is considered by some to be an ill-defined word, that is "instinct," usually follows a fairly well-defined pattern for a given species. Individuals of a species build nests which are usually identifiable as being built by a bird belonging to that species. The material used for the nest, and the design, usually are typical. Where there is variation it may be put down to lack of experience in building, for the one-year-old birds are not always able to build perfectly the first time. (I remember that the first nest of blue jay Lady was not by any means a perfect nest, nor was the second, although better than the first; the third and the later nests were perfect for the species.)

Individual behaviour is not so circumscribed. In fact, it would be remarkable to find two birds alike in characteristics and temperament. No two of a group of thirteen bluebirds under my care are alike in disposition. The morning I began to rear Joey and Jodee, both were eight days old. There is no need to tell you more of trustful Joey. After ten years of caring for Jodee, although he would alight on my hand, he mistrusted me to such an extent that the slightest move on my part would send him off. While on my hand he never lost his sense of

*As before, I mean by "authority" the professional ornithologist generally.

alertness, never failed to glance often at my face—in reality into my eyes; yet in all the years he had been given no cause to fear me, had never been held in my hand since a tiny youngster.

Nor is there need to tell you more of Little Blue and the younger Josie. Two of their youngsters though, both females, vary so greatly in disposition that to recognize them it is not necessary to place bands on their legs. The older is trustful, the younger as shy as old Jodee. Usually bluebirds do not fight with nor attempt to dominate birds of other species, although they are vicious fighters among themselves during breeding season. The older of Josie's two, although she does not show animosity towards any of the other bluebirds, is vicious in her attacks on robins, cardinals and other large birds if they happen to be eating from a food dish where she wishes to eat.

During the winter I keep a supply of sunflower seed in a feeder from which only the chickadees can secure the seed. A chickadee about to enter this feeder will immediately leave it if I appear with peanuts on my hand. One often picks out the larger half-kernel, another will take the smaller pieces, another will deliberately select from among many the kernel that suits its fancy (usually the whole kernel instead of the half which most like to take), and another almost invariably takes two half-kernels if they are not too large.

Scarlet the tanager will refuse a peanut of which he is very fond, if he wishes a raisin; or will refuse a raisin if he wishes a mealworm. The second Joey, when I am with him, will bathe only in a pail while standing on my hand. Bonnie junior will not bathe in the large water pan if there is a small one available. While I am changing water in the small bathing dishes of a bird which at the time must be caged, Bonnie insists on having his bath even when I am trying to rinse it out.

The mealworm box is in the storeroom, which is divided from the winter observatory by mesh wire. The instant I reach into the box there is a line-up of birds—some of whom have seen my action from nearly forty feet away—on a perch attached to the partition wire.

Scarlet, the male tanager, has a meal

Should I enter wearing a tie which is conspicuously different in colour from one I have been wearing regularly, Pat, the trustful cowbird, will go almost into a panic. Many trusting birds will not come near if I enter wearing a strange hat or garment. Years ago my first Vor the wood thrush (generally I retain the names of those who have gone), the most trustful of the many I have had, became ill. I looked at him one morning and knew he was dying. He opened his eyes, struggled to rise and crawled, literally crawled, to my hand where he snuggled for a moment and died.

Billy was a European bullfinch and Judy was his mate. Billy was stung in the mouth by a yellow-jacket wasp and died in twenty minutes. That left Judy with five two-day-old nestlings to rear. Copious saliva is mixed with the food of these nestlings by the parents. For some unknown reason the need for saliva and her ceaseless efforts to feed all five made her ill. Usually in giving medicine to a bird that is very ill the beak must be held open and the medicine put into the throat or the crop. Not once was this necessary with Judy. She disliked intensely the medicine I offered but, improbable as it may seem, opened her bill when I coaxed and allowed me to put the medicine into her mouth from a dropper. I must admit that at times I had to call her by name repeatedly, but not once did she fail to respond in the end. Beauty, the evening grosbeak, was ill twice in her very long life. Because of their powerful muscles it is exceedingly difficult to force open the bills of these birds. I did not need to do so with Beauty. She responded to coaxing as did Judy.

A green heron so covered with oil that it could neither fly nor walk was brought to me. In its fear of man it was so vicious that I had to protect my hands with leather gloves. But only three times did I have to do so before it accepted my attentions without the slightest showing of fear and, instead of driving its bill at my hand, gently took my fingers in its mandibles. It was unable to drink from a vessel, and I tried to give it water from a spoon. So greatly did it want a drink that it tried to seize the spoon, thus spilling the water. In a surprisingly short time it learned that if it held its bill open the water would be poured into its mouth.

These are only a few of many examples of wide variation or free choice of conduct. Do they not show that there is no rigid pattern as there is where instinct only rules?

When we are considering motives for specific behaviour it seems to me we should be careful in our analysis not to jump to hasty conclusions, but to dig as deeply as possible. An experiment has been made in which a song sparrow of "weak" character was placed in

122

a cage and put in the territory of a dominant sparrow. The weak bird, through extreme fear, dropped dead when the dominant one seized it by its feathers.

Here our first reaction may be to consider this behaviour as absurd and unintelligent. But in what way was it more absurd and unintelligent than a similar demonstration in man, except that man probably would not die of fright? Here was complete panic induced by fear in one bird and blind rage in the other. This rage was caused by the intrusion of one sparrow into the territory of another. Territorial rights are strenuously defended by most species of birds—certainly by all songbirds which stake out individual territory in the nesting season. But although it may have been absurd, just as it would be in the case of a human being, there is nothing which proves lack of intelligence.

Many an intelligent man has beaten on the bars of his prison cage in frenzy while overcome with emotion. It is well known that blind rage can so overcome man that all thoughts of a logical course of conduct are eliminated from his mind. The behaviour of these two birds was not proof of lack of intelligence but proof of two dominant emotions being present. The weak bird was probably, as are all wild birds when caged, in a panic of fear when placed in the cage and this fear was so intensified by the presence and attack of a stronger bird that fear became frenzy.

Another experiment was made with redstarts as the subjects. The young were taken from the nest and held in the hand where the parents could see them. The male came to the hand holding the nestlings and fed them, but the female, apparently, would let her nestlings starve rather than trust a human hand.

The question here seems to be not lack of intelligence, as has been suggested, but entirely a matter of the degree of fear shown by each. The fear of man, although almost universal among our songbirds, varies in degree from an entire absence—seen rarely—to fear so great as to cause death. In the male, fear of man was sufficiently limited to allow the feeding instinct to remain dominant. In the female it was the reverse. Sometimes both parents may abandon the young under similar circumstances, thus showing that the nesting rhythm of both has been destroyed for the present.

Although exceedingly rare among birds that know man well, entire lack of fear may be inherent in some individuals as shown by my experience with a family of young house wrens. In the garden a pair of house wrens nested. When their five nestlings became old enough to reach the entrance of their nest box they showed no fear

Two of the five fearless baby house wrens

while being fed insects with the fingers. After they left their nest shelter a visitor and I fed the nestlings. While we did so the parents at no time uttered the scolding notes characteristic of these wrens. Gradually the family of young followed their parents farther afield. We followed and I picked up one of the youngsters, which perched on my finger, chirped, but showed no sign of fear. Each of the others was handled and fed insects. When a finger was put under the breast of any one of the five, it would hop upon it. With all our handling, photographing, and feeding of the young, the parents, who remained close at hand, showed no signs of being disturbed.

This lack of fear or the frenzy of fear shown by the robin and song sparrow has in my opinion no bearing whatever on the question of intelligence any more than would the paralyzing fear of snakes shown by some human being be a criterion of intelligence.

124

Not Too Close, Dick

Blue jay Dick was eight years old; his mate, Pet, was seven. Uno was seven and Lady eight when they left us for good. All their years they had been with me and they and their young had lived together in almost complete amity. But for all their good nature, the imp of jealousy took possession of Dick and Uno occasionally, although its display was mild and never led to quarrelling.

As I look back over the years, I still can see Lady on a roost as Dick comes into the shelter from the storm of snow outside. For a moment Uno intently watches as Dick alights near Lady, then flies to her side, crowds close to her and pecks her gently. As though to reprove her mildly for allowing Dick to roost so close, he addresses her with low, gurgling notes as his feet beat a soft tattoo upon the perch. Lady pays no heed: she is not encouraging Dick, nor has Dick any flirtatious intentions. But it is plain to see that Uno is mildly jealous of Dick's nearness, gentle as he is in his objections. Much more serious were Dick's objections when as his son took undue liberties.

Zulu was a female crow and knew a different kind of jealousy from that of Uno, although it was no different except for its peculiarity. Zulu was exceedingly fond of me, so fond in fact that if I had the time—which of course I never had—she would have let me fondle her for hours. No amount of teasing would induce her to bite or peck unless I teased her after she had gone to roost and had become quite sleepy.

Rarely do we see a domestic fowl that enjoys the same kind of petting Zulu craved; but I had one, a Japanese silky bantam, that thoroughly enjoyed having her feathers stroked. Often Zulu and the silky hunted insects on the lawn. Should Zulu see me pet the silky,

125

she would slowly approach with half-extended wings, bow low as she uttered deep guttural notes and when she reached me would strike me forcefully on the ankles, eyeing the bantam all the while. If I persisted, she would then viciously attack the bantam who, although she showed no trace of jealousy, was more than willing to take up Zulu's challenge, for her hatred of Zulu was intense. I always had to separate them and take one away, for otherwise jealousy and hatred would have led to serious hurts to both.

A more peculiar phase of what we term jealousy in human beings was somewhat more disturbing and just as comical as Zulu's strong emotion. Many years ago, Rollo, a young Mexican yellow-headed parrot, came to make his home with me and brought with him a gradually developing temper which years of attempted petting never altered. Not only did he never show affection but viciously objected to any familiarity. Even to touch his feathers was inviting most painful reprisals.

A year-old child and her mother visited us one day and, like all babies, she had to crawl about the floor. Rollo, also on the floor, stared for a moment at the baby and then began his waddling way towards her. Fearing he might bite her, my mother, who always attended to Rollo's wants, picked her up. Rollo's temper flared; he scrambled up my mother's skirt until he reached her lap and without more ado gave her an unexpected and vicious bite. She literally threw him off her lap and handed the baby to the mother. This rebuff did not bother Rollo for now he proceeded to climb again. We did not know it then, but he wanted to play with that baby. Later we found out that this same little one was as safe with him as with her mother. Any child, but particularly a very young one, could pull his feathers out, stretch his wings and roll him upon the floor. It was all fun to Rollo. But let an adult interfere or attempt to take the child away and his temper flared. The iris of his eyes contracted to pin-point size as an almost insane jealousy took possession of him.

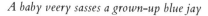
A baby veery sasses a grown-up blue jay

How Can We Measure?

Perhaps most of us have had the experience of meeting someone whom we instantly disliked, although the reason for this dislike we could not explain even to ourselves. Is this mysterious and instant reaction in a bird more curious than when seen in ourselves? In what way is it different, except for our restraint, from the occasional unexplainable antipathy of one human being for another?

Some, believing that owls never harm blue jays, seem unable to understand the undoubted antipathy of these birds for owls and place this emotion with the inexplicable. But this particular feeling is readily explainable. My observations lead me to believe that the screech owl is the most usual target for the jay, and the jay's hatred for this bird is based upon dearly bought experience, as a study of the subject itself will show.

The observatory in which Dick and Pet, Uno and Lady, were quartered during part of the winter was built of one-inch mesh wire. Many, many times when these screaming blue jays awakened me in the night, I dressed and rushed to the observatory to find a screech owl with its talons either grasping a jay by the breast or the head, or trying to reach one through the wire. Is it not probable that wild jays are subject to the same attacks?

A stronger emotion than antipathy—enmity—shapes the behaviour patterns of birds as it does of men. Although we cannot analyze it—if it can be analyzed—as readily as we can in "our higher order," it seems nevertheless to take the same form. It is modified in measure for the reason that birds are not capable of the range of endeavour of man. So far as we know they have no way of expressing enmity in full, other than by combat. Whereas man, with his inventive and devious mind, has a hundred ways.

127

Even though they are much larger, wood thrushes do not attempt to dominate bluebirds; do not show animosity toward them. Therefore there was no apparent reason why the younger, and later, Josie the bluebird should show such a dislike for two of these thrushes. She had no aversion for the smaller veery and hermit thrushes, near her own size, but she had what amounted to a much stronger emotion for Vor and another, a female, wood thrush. Her antipathy for Vor drove him from his rightful feeding ground one summer. A still stronger emotion possessed her while in their winter home, for there she killed the hated female. These birds were with me all their lives and I knew them well, yet I could nowise account for Josie's bitter hatred of these two. Towards a hundred other birds of various kinds she showed no ill temper.

Why such enmity develops or exists we do not know any more than we always know the reason it develops in ourselves. Even inference will not tell us why one son of Josie was hated by Little Blue and unusual friendship was shown for her other son. You will recall that although these two were Josie's sons, they were not sons of Little Blue but of Jodee, her mate of another year; how during all the winter Little Blue had shown animosity toward one and exceptional liking for the other; how this same situation persisted in spring and culminated in summer in silent yet dangerous conflict.

We have no way of measuring this behaviour of Little Blue. Josie's younger son had never shown ill will towards him. Antipathy, enmity, animosity, hatred, anger are all so closely allied yet so difficult to separate in our quest for knowledge of the ways of birds. Papeek, Weewee and Cherilee, the white robins, free of restraint were ever demonstrating towards one another what seemed to be animosity. As we learn more of the reasons for this and that, we can understand the combative spirit seemingly so necessary in breeding seasons; but why this trait should be prolonged through fall and winter months is beyond our comprehension, except among those species where a "peck order" may be established. No such order seems to have been established among the nine robins in the observatory.

Pugnaciousness, a dominant characteristic, is more extreme in robins than in most of the songbirds with which I have had to deal. With it is combined often aggressiveness uncontrolled, or perhaps uncontrollable, for they show evidence of a more primitive intelligence than most, as I have noted before. Such aggressiveness was, however, much more intense in these albinos than in most others of their kind. So evenly matched in strength were they, so aware, it would appear, of each other's nature that their almost continual spats did not

128

lead to domination of one over another; thus no serious harm was done. Were this aggressiveness confined to their own kind, as it is in the wood thrushes, we might better understand; but it was not. They did not usually fight with other birds. Yet, during the first few years of their lives no smaller bird was safe from what we would call treacherous attack.

Perhaps we can more easily explain the extreme irritation of Sherr, the rose-breasted grosbeak, when the full-grown youngsters begged him for food which he intended they should hunt for themselves. But how explain the distaste even for their close company which developed? This distaste or aversion for close contact extended to his mate and all others of his kind in their association through fall and winter months. Not only was this aversion inherent in Sherr, but in his mate and all their kindred. However, this emotion is mild and does not lead to strife.

During most seasons of the year, barely-perceptible to strong aversion is shown often towards other birds by many of those I have come to know. Usually this is more pronounced between individuals of a kind than between individuals of different species. Except during breeding seasons we rarely see this display among such birds as cedar waxwings. These gentle-natured birds show, at times, a mild aversion to having another of their kind too close to them as they roost. Such a thing as combat does not, however, take place.

Fuss, the catbird, and his mate may be feeding peaceably from the same food dish. Suddenly Fuss gives his mate a vicious peck. She immediately retaliates by attacking him, and a fight ensues. This attack is not serious and is quickly forgotten by both. Here we have displayed resentment at what looks like an uncalled-for piece of maliciousness on his part. Such action by Fuss could not happen of course during nuptial life, for then both are gentleness itself toward each other. Their union precludes all possibility of quarrel. That phase of their lives necessitates full co-operation, loss of all disrupting emotions, that their race may live. They, on their lower plane, have not become "civilized"; therefore do not indulge in spats, or worse, while carrying on the duties of home life.

Like so many of our songbirds—not all—Fuss does not take a mate for life. When nesting duties have passed into the limbo of forgotten things for them (it is presumption on our part to say these things are forgotten, even if it be so), usually they live peaceful lives. But Fuss and all his clan are subject to fits of vicious rancour, murderous and persistent temper which has no mercy.

Fuss himself is getting old, although he does not show it, and age

129

Three albino robins share a meal with two European blackbirds, two mountain bluebirds, three robins, a cedar waxwing and a female cowbird

seems to have mellowed him. For several years he has been as gentle with his own and with all other birds as Scarlet the tanager, or Ori the oriole. As has been, for two whole years or more, the present mate of Fuss. Yet only a short time ago, as I was watching her, I noticed her lowered and rapidly vibrating wings, her open bill, and heard from her a note I know—sure signs of unfolding temper in a catbird. I nearly paid for my scant attention (not since a youngster had she showed signs of ill will) by nearly losing Fuss. She had him on the floor, his eyes full of sand, his spirit gone, his body utterly exhausted, when I drove her off. Although I did not see it, I knew what she had done. Her mounting rage had frightened him—it was for him only, not for any other bird—and he had retreated from her. That was all she needed to know. She drove him with persistence until he tired—tired more from fright than flight—then she pounced. Had I not happened to be there—no more Fuss.

This rancour, if that is what it is, seems to be a somewhat sudden acquisition and may continue for several days. While this emotion possesses it, a catbird may attack other birds, but such attacks do not seem to persist; there seems to be no ill will toward them. Do not judge the mate of Fuss the catbird harshly. She and all her kind have many lovable ways. We too have fits of rage at times. And a few days in prison for Fuss's mate and she may take her former place among all the others, to be free—possibly—from exhibitions of rancour for many a day.

130

Like Papeek and his brother and sister; like wood thrush Vor and Vee, his mate of another year, and the others of his tribe; like Veery and his kind and the hermit thrushes, all these of wondrous song, all have pugnacious dispositions, varying in degree. Throughout the daylight hours there is almost continual strife among them but, except for veeries, only with their own species. Rarely are there serious results. Perhaps it is only strenuous play.

Vor and Vee the wood thrushes will face each other, maybe a foot or more between, head and breast low, a sudden flip of wings as they call a sharp "quitt, quitt," then simultaneous attack as they come together in the air just above the ground. Sometimes a few feathers fly and by spring their tails may be broken off short and much bareness may show around the eyes where feathers have been pulled. But the eyes of birds are rarely, if ever, pecked even during the most ferocious fighting. To injure the eye would seem to be beneath a songbird. Should it be Veery I am watching, I will see him with wings held tight, breast puffed out, his head with feathers close, extended straight forward and bill wide open, as he taps the earth alternately with rapidly dancing feet. Then, a rapid run as he attacks. His attack is just as apt to be against a larger bird, a wood thrush, but never against a smaller one. Our hermit thrush, too, crouches low, often a few inches from another, wings slightly drooped, rapidly vibrating; tail flicking up and down, eyes half closed as though waiting for an opportune moment for a sally, while *one foot* rapidly and continuously taps the ground. No harm is ever done, nor will he fight or play with others than his own. With none of the *Hylocichla* thrushes does there seem to be continued dominance of one over another, or of what is called the "peck order" of fowls.

I have said we have no way of measuring the behaviour of Little Blue. Nor can we measure the behaviour of Phalus the black-headed grosbeak, behaviour that does not seem due to enmity or any other allied causes. In all ways except one he is as gentle-natured as Sherr and all his clan. Related so closely to rose-breasted grosbeaks that mating sometimes takes place where the two species meet in the West, so closely that their songs are nearly the same, one would expect a like disposition. I have found this to be so except for one unexplainable trait, a trait that others also have found. While standing quietly on a roost Phalus will reach under a bird that is near and give a quick bite on the leg—no other place. His bite is so powerful that a broken leg is sometimes the result. It is not an attack, as we expect, of one bird on another. It is not retaliation for some untoward move on the part of the other. It is just one of those queer imponderables we find in a bird.

131

How different the behaviour of Vesper and Tana and Beauty, the evening grosbeaks, with bills so powerful that one bite could take the leg off rather than break it. But not a mean trait do they show. Still it would seem that evening grosbeaks can have and demonstrate real anger—before they come to know us well.

These birds come to visit us rarely here. Perhaps they will visit us only once every four or five years. Of the seventy or more that stayed a large part of one winter, twenty-five were coaxed into the breeding observatory, which in winter is usually empty of birds. These grosbeaks were to be banded with wildlife bands. As each bird was banded it was freed through a small exit gate used by nesting birds in summer.

An almost unbelievable incident was ours to enjoy, yes and to wonder over, after one of these males was banded. When freed through the gate he flew three feet away, instantly turned and flew back to the hand that had banded him, bit that hand hard and then off to the trees. Frightened and panic-stricken as he apparently was, anger overcame his fear. Perhaps that was not anger but, if not, then what was it? Merely a "conditioned reflex"? Wild and frightened and angry; yet, had we kept him, how would he in future years have reacted to human company? Evening grosbeaks Tana, Tina, Cherree and Beauty, have given you the answer.

The bluebird has won the race with the female rose-breasted grosbeak for a mealworm (seen just below his bill)

I Don't Care—or Do I?

Of all the emotions, the one considered supreme in man, compassion, is rarely, if ever, seen in birds. Yet we cannot be sure that it is absent in our feathered friends. Because of their inherent selfishness, it is adjudged by many authorities that birds are entirely lacking in this emotion, among others. In fact, even to suggest that a bird may have such emotion is to invite—well, derision. You will remember however, how the hungry youngsters of Rée-e the rose-breasted grosbeak, attracted the attention of Sherr; how, disregarding his own for a few moments, he fed them and I described his actions as seeming compassion. Describing his behaviour as such will, in all probability, engender criticism; and possibly even the charge of fatuity. It may be contended by some that the screaming cries of the young proved a stimulus which overcame Sherr's impulse to carry food to his own young ones: that he was confused by the exceptionally intense food calls.

In trying to determine the emotion aroused we must examine closely his actions. Loud hunger calls did no more than attract his attention: cause him to pause on his platform and stare at the young each time he returned from the trees with food for his own. Such pauses showed awareness, not confusion. Later hunger-calls turned to screams as the four youngsters stretched high in the nest. Sherr, who alone was caring for his own nestlings, just about to enter his compartment, paused longer than usual, turned from the entrance (from his own hungry young), flew up over the top of the observatory and down the far side to the other entrance—and into strictly forbidden territory—where he fed the four starving youngsters.

Not once but several times Sherr repeated his good deed, each time alighting first on his own platform and listening. Would it not seem reasonable to assume that, if the screaming calls had overcome by mechanical reaction the inherent impulse to feed his own nestlings, he would have flown from the nearby tree directly to his neighbour's nest? His pause on the platform indicated a conscious change of plan in contradistinction to an instinctive reaction.

That Sherr was confused by the screams does not seem to be a tenable explanation. Rée-e's nest was only some fifteen feet from his own and he could see it through the mesh wire. Had he been confused by the screams of the hungry youngsters, he would have tried to fly by the most direct route toward the nest *through* his own compartment. Instead of confusion I see intelligent awareness that the wire partition would prevent his reaching the nest. And more than this, although he never had been in Rée-e's compartment before, he knew the exact location of the entrance; the route he would have to take to arrive there and the location of the exit. The fact that there was no hesitation clearly shows lack of confusion.

That the screaming cries of the young proved a stimulus which overcame his impulse to feed his own (a natural reaction) may be the answer, but seems far-fetched for the reason that, although his own did not scream, they too called as soon as they saw him. Nor were these calls weak, Sherr's nestlings being almost the same age as those of Rée-e and all half grown. Perhaps it was not compassion. I do not know for Sherr refused to tell me.

Mealtime comes often for this little fellow

I Too Have Courage

Among birds, as among us, there are dominant characters and weak characters and in-between gradations. So too with birds. We will find attempted domination a much stronger trait in one than in another. Nor is it a seasonal phenomenon but one that often persists throughout the year, although varied in degree in different seasons. And, as with us, although at times backed by courage it is achieved largely by bluff. Often in a species it is established through fighting—where strength may be a factor—but not to the extent that strength would determine priority among men. Usually there is comparatively little difference in either the weight or size of two adult birds of a species. Therefore it seems to be some mental rather than physical strength which is the determining factor. Some inner quality of superiority during combat achieves the desired end. This quality however is not necessarily present in a later fight. Thus persistent dominance seems to be rarely accomplished among the species I have had under control.

This inner quality is well demonstrated by Vor the male wood thrush. Because cats had climbed to the top of the summer observatory one night in early winter, so frightening the four blue jays that two of them were killed when they dashed blindly into posts, the two remaining were moved to the winter observatory. Blue jays, notwithstanding their bad reputation, have gentle natures and can, generally, be trusted not to harm even the smallest bird, provided of course that it is not a callow nestling (which some of them, not all, will steal). But, being larger birds and bolder than the others, they do not hesitate to grab.

Of all the thrushes Vor is the only one who will defy them and, although I could not say they are afraid of him, he has taught them great respect. The moment I appear in the winter home and offer some

135

favourite treat, these two jays (they are not named as I do not yet know their sex), without consideration for other birds, seize the food from my fingers. But if Vor happens to be there first, the feathers of his crown arise as with open bill he dares them to drive him off.

Of all the other birds only one, so far, has sufficient courage to attack so large a bird as a jay. Four-year-old Rée-e junior, a rose-breasted grosbeak, actually hates them and with a chip on his shoulder is more than ready for a test of strength whenever they come near. With feathers fluffed, wings partly spread and bill wide open, he screams and charges. He means it too, as well they know, and since they learned they never hesitate to retreat, for he is quite willing to take both on at once. This seems to be plain courage on his part, for not only is he a much smaller bird but also a gentle one with all the others in this winter home.

Ori the Baltimore oriole has courage also, but he lacks just the little more needed to keep the blue jays in their place. They anger him. To retreat is much against his will and, although at times he stands his ground, if they are too persistent he does retreat and expresses his irritation with angry and effusive chatter.

With gentle-natured birds such as cedar waxwings, attempted dominance usually seems to play a minor part. So subordinate is it that I cannot be sure that I have seen its presence except in nesting season. Even then it seems comparatively mild. It is not that waxwings add cowardice to their gentleness, for they do not. With that high crest and great open mouth which looks so formidable, they will defy much larger birds. But they never, in my experience, attempt to dominate others. Theirs seems to be a policy of "live and let live."

Perhaps there is no such thing as *permanent* dominance of one individual over another, or others of a species, among most songbirds. Some say it rules among our chickadees and it may be the rule among other species with which I have had no intimate acquaintance. But, among those I know well, fixed sway seems nonexistent.

The wood thrush is a trustful bird with visitors—especially when there is a treat in store

How Wild a Bird?

Flix the catbird was on the lawn, calling, calling for food. He appeared to be about three weeks old, not yet able to fly. It was thought by the one who first noticed him that his parents must have been killed, for, to judge by his insistent calling, he appeared to be very hungry indeed. With considerable difficulty he was caught, and now the fun began. When offered food he screamed, struggled and fought the food stick. No one was going to take care of him except his father and mother. Of course he had to be fed to live. The one who had picked him up knew how. Gently the slender black bill was forced open, the food stick with just a small amount of nestling food, placed deep in his throat—and he swallowed. Then a drop or so of water was allowed to trickle between the closed mandibles and he drank. But this was an indignity no baby bird of Flix's disposition intended to stand, so every time food was offered he protested that he would rather die than eat. Then, suddenly, one day shortly afterward he looked up straight into his lady's eyes, opened wide his bill and—how quickly that food now disappeared into the yellow throat. From that moment on fear never returned to Flix.

A little later he was brought to me and accepted me as he had his foster mother. More than that, to Flix all visitors were friends to be trusted. I have had many catbirds but none more lovable or gentle than this formerly wild youngster. Graceful and svelte in form, wonderful in song, gentle in disposition (there were no other catbirds here while he was here or perhaps he would not have been gentle with them), he was a favourite with everyone who came to know him. Perhaps for me he had what we know as affection, for my shoulder was a favourite place on which to ride—unfortunately. Sometimes I think he showed this affection by taking my finger gently in his bill, holding it there for seconds.

Often today I wonder where he is, if he is still alive; for I have not seen him for many months. This is the reason: I had put Sherree III, the female rose-breasted grosbeak, a tired, tired old lady of nearly eleven years (she was the granddaughter of the first Sherr and Sherree), with the other birds in the winter observatory where she was enjoying the freedom of that large space even though old age had tied her wings. In the morning I had found her head covered with blood, her eyes closed and many feathers lost. Some bird had attacked her early in the morning. I was afraid she was blinded and rushed with her into the house so that I might attend to her eyes at once. As I opened the kitchen door Flix flew from my shoulder. He had ridden there, all around to the back of the cottage, unknown to me. I could not leave Sherree to coax Flix back until I had satisfied myself that her eyes had not been damaged. When I did look for him he had disappeared. Perhaps a roving Cooper's hawk had passed at that moment when he left me; perhaps he had just wandered away, looking for the insect food he had not had for a long, long time: food that had enticed him farther and farther. Or perhaps when he hopped onto someone's hand he was imprisoned in a tiny cage, maybe never to be free again.

How different from Flix are those commonest of native birds, our robins, and our now somewhat-common year-around southerners, the cardinals. Many robin youngsters are brought to me: youngsters that should not be brought. A baby robin is seen on the lawn, calling, and immediately someone thinks it is lost.

With some a measure of fear has developed, yet most gain confidence very quickly. If the young robin happens to be a nestling fallen from the nest before fear has developed, it is not only as easy to feed as that of any species but, like the young wood thrush, it is an exceedingly appealing youngster with that odd motion of the head held partly sideways and lowered as it begs for food. Like most of our song-birds, these fledglings become independent at about thirty days, but unlike most they still coax and plead to be fed from the food stick or glass feeder for well on to a month or more. Gradually, for some unknown reason, fear of human beings returns until, at the age of two months or so, they become as wild or almost as wild as their parents. Seldom in all the years I have had robins have I had one that has remained trustful. Some, like pure-white Weewee and Robbie, a normally plumaged bird, would hesitatingly take a treat from my fingers and then only after they had been here for years.

Often I am puzzled by this, for as all of us know the robin seems such a companionable bird in the garden, follows the spade as we turn over the soil and rears its brood just over our head in some sheltered

138

Twilight descends and Fuss the catbird gets ready for bed

spot. Yet in the observatory now is a robin nearly twelve years old
who in some way fell out of his nest when only a day-old chick. He
was hand reared and brought to me. Does even this robin trust me?
Not at all.

Sometimes I wonder if it is because our robins are much less intelligent birds than most others, as I have found them to be in some ways.
Also the cardinals, another somewhat unintelligent species I sometimes think, are usually almost impossible to tame no matter at what
age they are brought. Yet when I think of our beautiful and gentle
cedar waxwings, seemingly less intelligent than most, this theory just
does not seem to apply—that is, among songbirds—for these birds
usually become trustful sooner than most others I know.

One spring a pair of those handsome whistlers, the cardinals, built
their nest about three feet from the ground in the arbor vitae just in
front of the porch. I could always see into the nest when I went down
the steps, for the female invariably left when I opened the door. One
morning I saw the nest empty and upon examining the ground underneath found the three squirming youngsters. What accident, if it was
an accident, tossed them out of the nest I could not imagine for they
were uninjured and the nest was not torn. I placed these little ones, as
naked as when they were hatched, back where they belonged. Neither
mother nor father would go near the nest. I hid from them but watched
until the youngsters were cold; took them into the house to warm and
put them back a number of times. The parents, excited, still refused to
go near; so I saw that if they were to live I must see to their needs.

139

Two of them did live and I knew from their appearance that one, which turned out to be a female, was five days old and her brother was six. At the time I took them to rear their eyes were still closed or just opening in slits, and of course, at this age, there were no signs of fear. Yet today, some years later, Kvar, the male, is as wild as any wild cardinal and his sister, Kvee, almost as wild.

Only once have I succeeded in taming a cardinal, the female "Redbird." For weeks she will come to my hand without hesitation; then suddenly, without reason or at least without any reason I know, will become as "wild as a hawk." She is utterly unpredictable. When I call "Redbird" she will come flying to me day after day; then, when I wish to show someone how tame a redbird can get, she will have nothing to do with me and this mistrust will persist for week after week.

One spring when Redbird was younger she reared a brood in a breeding compartment, then built her second nest some two hundred yards away on the other side of the brook. All the time she was incubating her eggs and rearing her young she visited here two or three times a day, always alighting on my hand for some favourite treat. What happened to her young ones I never knew but when summer was over she came back to her home and with her she brought her inexplicable behaviour. Redbird is too old to nest successfully now but she still is able to show me the ways of our cardinals.

The measure of confidence in a hand-reared bird varies between species and even between individuals, yes even between those from the same nest. Two nestling wood thrushes, a brother and sister, were about nine and eight days old when they came to me. The moment I offered the female her food she opened her beautiful orange mouth and accepted it as though she had known me always. Not a sign of fear was there. Her brother, a day older, crouched in fear, refused to be fed; I had to open his bill gently quite a number of times before fear left him. When these two were a month old I did not need to use the feeder for they knew whence the food came and were quite able to help themselves. But suddenly the sister, without apparent rhyme or reason, lost her trust in me while her brother just as suddenly trusted me in full and never lost this trust. Not during all the time the female was with me was she ever quite as trustful as was her brother.

There have been authentic instances where a wounded or frightened bird has gone to a human being for either succour or safety. You have learned of how bluebird Little Blue came to me for protection when bluebird Bonnie junior chased him almost to the point of exhaustion. But Little Blue was a hand-reared bird. Rajah the golden eagle was

Weewee, the female albino robin, as an adult

not. He was found shot through the leg and starving and was brought to me. As you have seen, for nearly five months I cleaned the wound and tended the injured leg; wound bandages around the badly injured joint; cut up his food and fed him with my fingers. Yet never during all that time did he once attempt to bite or use his swords of claws, even though I could not help but hurt him. How intently he watched me as I wound the bandage around his leg! As you read the story of Rajah you realized that had he not had some bird consciousness that he was being helped he could, and probably would, have put that great curved beak right through my hand.

Yet confidence and exceeding trust will not always keep one free from severe bites from some birds. Eleven-year-old Sherree, the female rose-breast, developed chronic catarrh some time ago and I occasionally have to use a very fine looped wire to remove the plugs from her nostrils. Of all the birds I have had no one has ever had more confidence in me than this third Sherree, except perhaps her daughter. Sherree can no longer bathe and I must clean her feathers. Now, too, her feet are tender and sometimes get dirty, for she can no longer reach a roost. I may take all this care of her, stroke her head and back, hold her in my closed hand, pinch that powerful bill in play. She takes it all in good part. But let her catch even a glimpse of the wire loop in its handle and she begins to cry—the rose-breast cry—and struggles in my hand. Now I really have to watch; for when my finger with the pipette is near her nostrils—a sudden twist of her head and she has my finger in an exceedingly painful grip. She means it too. The inside of her nostrils is very tender and, careful as I am, I know I hurt her. Sherree does not intend to be hurt if she can help it. By no means is this lack of confidence in me, but simply a protest at what she knows is forthcoming pain. Perhaps Rajah was a nobler bird, or more stoical.

Yet Beauty, the old evening grosbeak who greatly resented being held in the hand, would not under any circumstances bite me. Of all our smaller songbirds, the evening grosbeak has the largest and most powerful bill. Not only can they draw blood from a finger, but just as readily take out a piece of flesh. Yet of the many I have studied here, not one has ever attempted to bite me after it had made this place its home. They do not become trustful readily—sometimes it takes as much as three years to gain their complete confidence—but even so, if I have to handle one of these half-wild birds it will not bite.

Beauty was with me for many, many years; her trust in me was just as great as Sherree's but, resent handling as she might, like Rajah she would not retaliate when I hurt her. When she was nearly twelve years old, Papeek the young albino robin, exceedingly vicious with all the birds, tore the skin from the back of her neck exposing the vertebrae underneath. It was a large and painful wound. This flap of skin had to be sewn and taped in position so that it would heal. But during all this painful operation Beauty never once used her powerful bill on me. Nor did all the necessary handling to examine the wound take away in the least her confidence in me. She was very old at sixteen; had to be handled often then, but never lost her trustful ways. Often I wondered at that, for as age increased she became intolerant of other birds—not vicious, just crotchety.

This gaining of confidence—trust in a human being—is probably an

142

inexplicable process. We have no way to measure it except by comparison with ourselves. You will remember how Ori the Baltimore oriole gradually learned to trust me and then gave me the final test—a whack on the thumb with his needle-like bill before gently taking the peanut from between my fingers. He repeated this test for several days before he was absolutely sure of me. He has never whacked me since from lack of trust. But when I tease him now, by holding some favourite treat tightly between my fingers so that he cannot secure it, he will sometimes strike me hard. But that is supreme confidence. He knows I will not retaliate.

Occasionally other than songbirds are brought to me: birds that are sick or injured; birds that usually are more fearful of man than are many of our songbirds. One would expect to find such birds exceedingly difficult to tame, but this is not always so.

Rowing across the Miramichi River in New Brunswick, I saw a loon in a salmon trap. He could no more find his way out than could the salmon. Wild and frightened at being so close to man, each time

The author force-feeding a loon

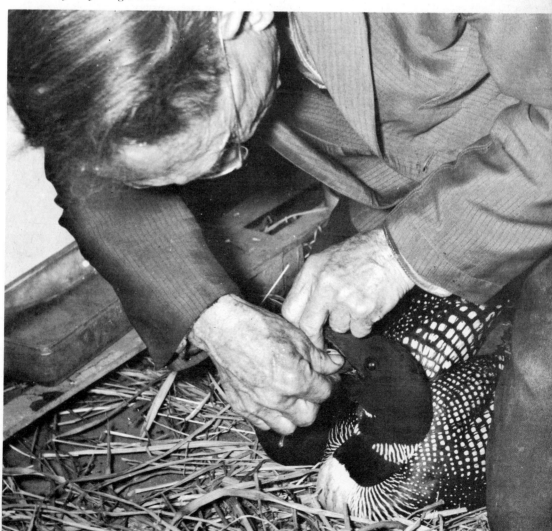

he surfaced he dived again. For so powerful and agile a swimmer there seemed only one thing for me to do: keep him diving until he exhausted himself. After an almost unbelievable number of dives I succeeded in wrapping a piece of net around him and, being curious about the behaviour of loons, took him to shore and placed him in a tiny pond in a brook. From there he was unable to fly or to dive.

Wishing to see just how a frightened loon would react in so limited a space, I held a small narrow board in front of him. He drove his bill so deeply into the wood I had to pull to release it. Had it been my hand instead he would have driven right through it. For a week only I kept him. Before the week was over he would answer me when I called, even though still out of sight. He would take my fingers gently in his bill, lift up a wing so that I might run my fingers through his soft white feathers, and allow me to stroke his beautiful head and back. Often I wish that I had studied the emotions of birds such as these along with the songbirds, for few adult songbirds have tamed so quickly as the few other species I have come to know.

Three orphan kestrels—the two males (juveniles) found starving,—the female on top taken from boys about to kill her

How Do They Know?

We often wonder, when we see male and female birds so alike in plumage that their sex cannot be determined by human eyes, how the birds themselves are able to discern the sex of others of their kind. One year, for lack of room in their summer home, a pair of wood thrushes remained in winter quarters. A compartment in the summer home, about one hundred feet away, had been allotted to Vor and Vee.

Wood thrushes do not mate for life and, although a female may choose the same mate for two or more successive seasons, her mate may interest himself in another female when breeding season is over. This interest, however, is brief. This year I moved Vor to winter quarters in late October. No sooner had he entered there than he flew close to the resident female, began to sing and court her in the quiet and dignified courtship of these birds. I knew her only by her banded leg, yet the moment he saw her in *late October* he recognized her sex.

Another time a strange catbird—I did not know her sex myself until later—was placed in the observatory in which were Fuss and his mate. Fuss was merely interested, but his mate at once attacked the stranger.

Introduction of a strange bird of any species creates sudden interest among all occupants. It matters not that the stranger belongs to a species already there. It is a *stranger* and its presence is resented. This resentment may be mild, or intense to the point of attack. An attack however is usually made by one of the same species as the one introduced. A strange hermit thrush, which to us looks much like other *Hylocichla* thrushes, when introduced into a mixed collection of these birds will be attacked at once by the hermits but not by

145

the veery or the olive-backed. Here we are mystified by such instantaneous recognition that the newly introduced bird does not belong.

Instantaneous, also, is the recognition of the difference between a person whom they know and a stranger. Although Sammy the wild blue jay will come close for the peanuts I toss, he will not come near if a stranger is close. To have a chickadee alight on his hand, to feel the cold little feet, is a thrill to many a visitor. Yet though one may stand by, in his hand the same treat I hold, often the chickadees will alight on my hand rather than on his. Often too they will not come to a stranger until I call them by name. Probably it is the voice or the clothes they recognize, but are we sure that is all? May they, too, not recognize the individual in a way similar to ours?

Possibly more mysterious is their recognition of hawks. All may be intense activity when suddenly Little Blue, Jodee or some other bluebird voices the alert: danger in the distance. I know the danger signal, gaze into the sky, and there, so far that I see only a speck, is a hawk: a dangerous hawk for small birds. Activity does not cease entirely, but is accompanied by extreme alertness. The hawk draws nearer and ever nearer. Suddenly the warning call, and all birds freeze. The hawk is in a dive straight for the trees nearby. But though the hawk comes nearer it stays high, as with quick wing-beats it circles. No sharp warning call is given, only the repeated alert. This is a Cooper's or perhaps a sharp-shinned hawk, both deadly enemies of birds.

Another time the alert is given. Over the meadow, "hedge-hopping," is a marsh hawk. It comes closer, but activity among the songbirds does not cease, nor does Little Blue sound the alarm.

As I stand among the birds I see Scarlet, the tanager, head turned to one side while he stares into the sky. As I watch I see others also glance skyward. There is no alert, no danger signal. I too look up and there I see, circling high above, a *Buteo*. There is no need for warning calls. Not one but knows this large hawk will not harm.

Many years have gone by since Scarlet looked up and taught me the lesson I learned. Now, so long afterwards, I find there is still more to be learned about hawks.

Two days before Christmas, as I looked out the window to watch the chickadees taking away sunflower seeds and downy wood-peckers pecking away at the suet which I had placed there, a large hawk swooped from a nearby tree and alighted on the feeder. I was astounded, as never before had I heard of a wild hawk visiting a feeding station. As I watched, this big bird, a red-tailed hawk (a *Buteo*) tried to eat the frozen suet. Knowing that hawks cannot digest fat I wondered! He must, for some reason, be starving. Then I saw him partly lose his balance as he tried to tear the suet.

Watching closely I saw that he was unable to use his right foot. It appeared swollen and dark where it should have been yellow, and the toes looked stiff and hard.

I cut off a piece of lean beef; walked slowly toward him, holding the meat so that he could see what it was. He allowed me to approach closely, my fingers holding the meat three inches away from his head. Starving as he was, that was too close. In graceful flight he landed on a near-by limb. I placed the meat on the feeder and quietly walked away. Immediately this big hungry bird flew to the feeder, clutched the red meat in the talons of his uninjured foot and filled his empty stomach. Five times that day I put meat on the feeder and each time I left he flew down to satisfy that gnawing hunger.

A red-tailed hawk as he came starving to the feeding station

147

Seeing that he had great difficulty in tearing the meat, I began cutting it in pieces so small that he did not need to pull them apart. Twice a day I put one hundred thousand international units of penicillin on one little piece in the hope that if he had some infection the antibiotic might clear it up.

For five days he roosted close by; watched as I placed more meat on the platform and, even while I was walking away, made an awkward landing—to gulp down another meal. From then on he came only twice a day and at this writing, some five weeks after, he still comes for his meals. In all probability he comes because he is unable to catch his own, which, at this time of year, consists entirely of that pest of the orchard—the meadow mouse.

What do the chickadees and woodpeckers have to say about this big fellow, with a wing-spread of over four feet, trespassing on their private preserve? Not a thing. Chickadees will alight within a foot of his beak to pick up a sunflower seed while the "downy" will calmly eat suet from a suet-holder hanging close by. They know that this big mouser, the farmer's best friend both in summer and in the long winter months, has no interest in them.

Those who study birds and know them well sometimes may be puzzled as to whether the hawk flying overhead is a sharp-shinned or a Cooper's. They are much alike in shape and flight, and a female sharp-shinned may be almost as large as a male Cooper's. But Dick and Uno the blue jays and all their kin seem to have no difficulties of this kind. At times when a sharp-shinned hawk has been near I have seen the jays excited, screaming as though in derision, not at all afraid. But let it be a Cooper's hawk so near, and there is utter silence as they seek the thick of the hawthorn.

As I write it is again toward the middle of winter. The deep snow on the ground and on the trees is hiding much of the food of birds. Seven blue jays are feasting on sunflower seeds, most of which I have placed in the wind-vane feeding station some fifteen feet from the window. The immediate vicinity is the home of Sammy, his mate, and another —probably, I am inclined to think, one of their youngsters of last year. The other four are strangers who come only during the cold and blustery days.

The feeder is open only in front. To secure seed a bird must go inside and from there it can see the approach of another in only one direction. While Sammy is inside his mate arrives. As she alights on the vane he turns in a flash, then instantly turns back to secure another seed as she joins him. His recognition of her is instantaneous. She fills her gullet with seeds and flies to the sumac to hide them. Another jay

148

arrives, alights on the vane and Sammy drives him out, but no farther than the perch or the vane. As Sammy will not let him in for the seed, he too flies away. Then a fourth bird arrives, from behind, and quick as a flash Sammy drives it into a hawthorn some twenty-five feet from the feeder. Not one stranger is allowed in the feeder or on it.

Here are a number of birds so alike I cannot tell them apart except for known characteristics of Sammy and his mate; yet recognition on their part is immediate—in the *middle of winter*. I often wonder at the reason behind this instantaneous recognition. Is it race consciousness, the experience gained by remote ancestors, handed down through the ages and fixed as an instinct? In so far as hawks are concerned it now seems instinctive. A fearless nestling, hand-reared away from adults of any species, does not seem to have to learn the difference between various species of hawks. Yet a predator almost as dangerous as a hawk, that fine songster and butcherbird of the north, the northern shrike, does not cause alarm among our resident birds when he first visits here in winter. They do not appear to know him instinctively as an enemy. They seem no more afraid of him than of a blue jay. Perhaps to them he seems a jay. Even the blue jays do not seem to recognize him as dangerous. Certainly they do not take him for one of their own kind. Yet I have seen a northern shrike try to kill a blue jay. It is one of our many puzzles while studying birds: instantaneous recognition of various species of hawks, yet no recognition of northern shrikes.

If those who believe there is no sex recognition whatever in birds except during the breeding season are right, then the birds' recognition of a behaviour pattern must be exceedingly acute, but I doubt if we are warranted in making a definite statement to that effect.

Although probably no two blue jays are alike in plumage, particularly in the pattern of the rectrices, it seems doubtful if identification through plumage would be so rapid as in the instance of Sammy and his mate. So far as I have been able to judge, birds that are mates so long as both live, such as blue jays, cardinals, white-breasted nuthatches and others, there is sex recognition all the year round. The possibility also of individual recognition should not be lost sight of. The subject has not been given sufficient study to allow us to determine *all the means* by which recognition takes place.

I Remember

In birds, as in ourselves, I suppose memory may be good, bad or indifferent; yet to state that it is very limited would not be in accordance with my observations.

One fall Lady joined a flock of migrating blue jays, and came back after being away for nearly a year. Not only did she remember me so well that she came directly to my shoulder but she went into the observatory with me, knew her mate as he did her, and showed every evidence of remembering the food dishes, the bath and her old roost: she was completely at home.

My first magpies—also named Buster and Dinah—very early in spring built a nest in the observatory. Their five young were taken by rats. They were then given liberty and nested in a tall hemlock nearby. This nest was robbed by raccoons. Shortly afterward I missed them; hunted the woods for miles around; then lost hope that I should ever see them again.

Late that summer news was brought that a pair of magpies were located some twenty-five miles away. When I arrived where I was told I should find them I could see their nest about fifteen feet up in a spruce which grew close to the house. As is the way with these birds, the nest was domed and the openings were in the sides. The nest was so bulky and the spruce so thick that I was unable to see inside. As I was looking at it the home-owner came near and I explained that I thought. the magpies were mine. She was quite unconvinced, partly I think because she had become fond of these birds and did not like the thought of their being taken away. To prove they were mine I called "Dinah!" A head showed in the entrance in one side of the nest; then, as I called again, Dinah came all the way out, flew to the ground at my feet, spread quivering wings and bowed her head up and down, greeting me with such evident pleasure that the homeowner immediately said, "These birds are not mine, they are yours."

I took from them three of their four, leaving one. Later I was told —I did not visit again at that time—that all three made their home in the spruce; still later, that the young bird disappeared. One day in late fall Dinah came home—alone—stayed a short time, then departed. For some time she continued making short calls and I, wondering why she was always alone, visited her home in the spruce only to learn that Buster had been killed by an owl. Dinah, to find out if Buster was here, had flown that twenty-five miles a great number of times, never satisfied, always seeking her mate.

And the blue jay Lady! She was far off for nearly a year. Remember also the chickadees "Deedee," "The Tapper," and the "Pocket Dee-dee." May it not be said that the memory of birds is not so limited as some would have us believe, but is remarkably good?

Blue jays Dick and Lady, twelve days old, and still under the parental roof

Will You Play with Me?

Always waiting for me as I came up the path from some trip beyond the garden was Zulu, the crow. Undoubtedly she waited often for the petting she expected each time I was near, but also she waited to play. Her playing was simple: much like that of a dog. As I approached to within a few feet she would pick up a small twig, a leaf, or perhaps snip off a flower—she was inordinately fond of cutting my daffodils—and coax me to take it from her. If I attempted to snatch it, a sudden swift turn of her head kept it out of my reach. Then, if I drew back my hand, she again held the twig within inches, her eyes watching sharply for my slightest move. Rarely was I quick enough to grasp what she held, but if I did there was a tussle to see who would retain it. Usually the only way I could outmanoeuvre her was to throw several twigs down and outguess her as to which I intended to snatch.

I think that in her mind there was the same kind of play when she helped me to pull weeds in the garden. Usually she helped with each that I pulled but sometimes saw another which ought also to come up, and this one she pulled herself. The difficulty with this kind of play was that her choice was just as likely as not to be a plant I intended to let grow.

Like Papeek, the albino robin, and Merul, the European blackbird (a close relative of our robin), she played a game all by herself. This game was an erratic flight back and forth on the ground or a few inches above it: a dodging half-dance at the side of some shrub.

A simple game too is played by all cedar waxwings. A small object, sometimes a pebble, will be picked up by one and passed to another. This other will dance away a few inches, the pebble in its bill, and then back to give it to the first. For many minutes the game will go on, the object being passed back and forth.

152

What? No cherries? (Cedar waxwings)

Some ornithologists insist that this is merely a form of courtship feeding. Were it performed by a known pair or between a known male and female only, this inference might be logical. Certainly court-ship feeding is a habit of these birds. However, I have seen the per-formance many times in which five birds standing in a row have taken part, the object being passed from one to another and then passed back. Not always was the object passed to each in turn down the line and then back, but all took part in the game.

That this is play, and that playfulness is as inherent in some birds as any other characteristic, is indicated by the behaviour of a waxwing —the only one I had at the time—several years ago. Redbird, the cardinal, stood on a wild grapevine which stretched from one end of the winter home to the other. The waxwing flew up with a small object, probably a pebble, and tried to give it to Redbird. Redbird took the pebble gently and seemed to pass it back. I could not be sure that he did give it back, but I could see that the waxwing expected it. I could see also that Redbird was a little confused, for he did not know this game, but he did turn his head, still holding the pebble, as though he was giving it to the waxwing.

153

Buster the magpie—ready for a fight

Buster the magpie had a wicked game he loved to play. Usually when I went for the mail he accompanied me, but unlike the blue jays, did not often ride on my shoulder. He knew another way in which he could have much better sport. Flying behind and much above, where I could not watch him well, he would make a sudden dive and that heavy bill of his found its mark on that favoured spot—the back' of my neck.

Like Zulu, he was fond of playing with me, but was ever ready with vicious temper to turn that play into combat in which he used both feet, as well as a powerful beak. The back of my hands were always scarred while he was with me. His name was the only word he used clearly; and when he fought with me, the more he lost his temper, the more often he uttered a deep, throaty "Buster, Buster."

154

For as Long as We Live

It has always been pleasant to look back over the past and recall the gentleness, the affection and *faithfulness* shown by Uno and Lady; by the first Vor and Vee; by the first Joey and Josie. Am I mistaken in my memories? Some students of bird behaviour deny that the great majority of songbirds are devoted and faithful to their mates and young, and assert that their usual behaviour pattern is exceedingly low, in conformance with their lack of a code of ethics. Certainly we could readily believe that there was no code of ethics among house wrens, but to use the wren as an illustration of a lack of morals among birds in general would be as indefensible as it would be to use as an example the morality of some of the human race as depicting the whole. The house wren as a species is notorious for his philandering, yet no more notorious than many among the "the most remarkably evolved of a higher class."

My experiences with birds have led me to believe that the terms "devotion" and "faithfulness" are entirely admissible. Certainly, some of our songbirds do remain mated pairs as long as both survive. Whether or not they subscribe to the precept of monogamy is impossible to prove—for they refuse to tell us. That during the breeding season most birds are faithful to their mates and young seems incontrovertible—so easily ascertained as to require no serious argument.

Some years ago a cold-blooded experiment was carried out, possibly with the view of endeavouring to show the faithlessness of birds. The male of a mated pair of indigo buntings was shot and it was found that the female secured another mate the next day. This male too was shot. According to this perplexing tale each time the female lost her mate she secured another and each time she did so the new mate was shot until in all nine males were destroyed. Her tenth mate was allowed to live.

155

This female bunting has been compared to a woman who, conjecturally, might have ten husbands in one summer. Even if there were such an incredible number of unattached males in the vicinity of her nest, this would not, to me, be a good example of the faithlessness of mates.

The natural and insistent urge to reproduce their kind is probably the most outstanding characteristic of birds. This urge seems to be the predominating essential in birds at certain seasons of the year and seems to be more predominant than in many human beings. To imply that it had anything to do with the normal life of the bunting appears to me to be inept.

The fact of the matter would seem to be that succeeding mates were sought probably for one purpose only—the fertilizing of her eggs. Had the cruel experiment been made after all her eggs were laid, in all probability the bunting would have carried on alone. Yet, if a comparison must be made, our civilization—at least a large part of it—worships at the feet of many of "our remarkably evolved species" whose morals do not seem to be on a higher plane.

I am not a sentimental bird lover; I hold no brief for such, only in so far as I feel that they are at least innocuous. I am imbued however, with considerable sentiment where birds are concerned, which is a very different matter. Sympathetic understanding is, it seems to me, engendered and aided by deep attachment and such attachment does not necessarily warp discernment. Such understanding seems necessary when we try to dissect the motives of birds—such as that of the female indigo bunting.

Casual observations can lead to error. To generalize, also, often leads to error. It would seem to be an error to group all species of birds together by stating that, when the death of a mate takes place, the living one of the pair shows little evidence of loss and that recollection of loss is exceedingly limited. If it is possible to determine with any degree of exactitude that such is or is not the case, intimacy with the bird concerned is a necessity.

Redbird, the cardinal, and his mate were not satisfied with any nesting site I supplied. Therefore, so that they might choose a site to their liking, I gave them liberty. Their first nest was in a hawthorn about a hundred yards away; the second nest in a hawthorn not far from the first and their third in a grape-vine-covered tree about one hundred and fifty yards from the first and close by the lane.

One evening as I was passing down the lane I could see Redbird's mate sitting on her nest. Next morning, not far from the second nest, I heard Redbird whistling loudly. His song was much louder than usual

156

Redbird the cardinal's mate with her nestlings

at this late time of year and more continuous than I had heard for weeks. For a while I watched him, wondered at his excessive song, then went to his mate's nest. His mate could not be seen. Several times during the next few hours I visited the tree in which she had built her nest but she was not there. I climbed the tree and found three eggs—stone cold. Either during the night or early morning, apparently, some predator had killed her.

Not only all that day but for two and a half days altogether, their territory, some two acres in extent, was searched by Redbird. The third nest, the two previous nest sites and the summer home of my other birds, where Redbird and his mate spent their winters, were visited in turn. From dawn to dark he sang almost continuously. As the season of song was nearly over other cardinals answered only at long intervals. Instantaneous forgetfulness? Before returning to his normal life, two and a half days—two and a half years for a human being? A matter of degree only.

Buster junior played with me, fought with me, with exuberant zest. One morning, early, a great horned owl swooped, frightened his mate Dinah junior and him into a panic. Dinah flew against and clung to the two-inch-mesh wire which enclosed their home. Again the owl struck. Late that morning Dinah died in my hands. From that day until Buster died, some two months after—he had not been injured, showed no signs of illness—he never talked again, never played or fought with me as in the past; showed a lassitude and lack of interest in life exceptional in a bird of this species. Why? Who knows? Perhaps the obvious conclusion will be called "nonsense," "absurd," "naive"; yet will these words answer the question?

To say that consciousness of tragedy—if I may use that phrase—is entirely absent is mere conjecture and incapable of proof. If it *is* present in some instances as seems indicated by the cardinal and magpie, it may be present in many or all, yet be so ephemeral that it may escape notice.

157

We Wonder and Surmise

I have told you much of these birds so that you will come to know (and in your consciousness will remain always the knowledge) that our songbirds are more than merely "birds." Too often the expression is, "Oh, it is only a bird." They are not of our flesh, nor do they live on our plane, but in many ways they seem akin to us. They do not speak our language, nor we theirs. We never can have a full understanding of the various processes of their minds. Perhaps the most we can do is to wonder and surmise. Perhaps no surmise is so tenable as that engendered by close companionship with trustful birds, for they hold back no secrets even if many of these secrets are, for us, unsolvable.

Although my studies have led me to conclusions contrary to the conclusions of many, I wish to emphasize that in no way have such studies led to the contention that birds equal or even distantly approach man in capacity. My point is not: "Have they intelligence even distantly approaching that of man?" but "Have they intelligence and emotions *akin* to man's?" It is my suggestion that, although ruled by instinct to a much greater extent than man, most of our songbirds not only have capacity—small as that capacity may be—for more than a glimmer of intelligence, but, even though it be on a low plane compared to ours, it may logically be compared with that of man; that their emotions are, basically, similar to those of man. The longer I know birds and the better I know them the more I am convinced that we can, with confidence, compare most of their traits with our own, rudimentary as their traits undoubtedly are.

In point of fact, if we concede that Buster and Dinah, the magpies, worked out a plan whereby they could gain satisfaction and we are unable or unwilling to compare the inception of that plan to the inception of any plan in the mind of man, then with what can we compare it?

158

That there is great variation between species, just as there is between human races, is evident; also that there is variation between individuals, just as in mankind, although in birds perhaps less pronounced.

Some believe that the real truth would be that they appear to be closer to automatons than to intelligent animals. This seems tenable on the ground that instinct—to use the word in its broadest sense—controls a greater part of their activities than it does in man. My studies have not been concerned with degree but with the question of whether or not any species of passerine bird is endowed with perception—the power of reasoning, working out advantageous conduct under difficult or novel conditions—and the interaction of emotions.

To determine this we may examine their ability to learn. There are those who concede that birds can and do learn but that they do so very slowly, perhaps citing as an example the carelessness and stupidity of the robin, among other birds. In my estimation the robin may be classed among the least intelligent of songbirds, and, moreover, it is necessary to differentiate between race, or species, learning and individual learning.

Among many species of birds, individual learning is not only far from being very slow, but sometimes is very rapid. You have seen how quickly Tapper, the chickadee, learned how to signal when he wanted a peanut. Two other chickadees also clung to the window but neither of these learned to signal by tapping on the glass. To test his perception, his awareness of desire, I placed outside on the sill a small piece of bread (of which chickadees are fond), instead of a peanut kernel, and placed it just after he had signalled on glass. The bread was refused and the tapping on glass was resumed as soon as I entered the house. Here was shown decided discrimination, preference, and moreover what seems like belief that the use of a signal would result in satisfaction.

What does this learning imply? Manifestly the Tapper never used such a signal to induce other birds to supply his wants. What did he possess that others did not command? Obviously he had an ability to correlate two functions: to retain the pattern in his mind for nearly two years, and to retain, also, a consciousness of results.

Often during winter months I sit among the birds in close companionship. To the kin of Nara, the rose-breasted grosbeak, sunflower seeds are a favourite food. With their powerful bills they can hull a seed much quicker than I can with my fingers. Insectivorous birds also are fond of these seeds but, with their weaker bills, are unable to take off the husks. Always the favourite perch of Nara was my shoulder, and I handed many unhulled seeds to her while shelling others for some "soft-billed" bird on my knee.

159

Nara the rose-breasted grosbeak welcomes the author

On one such an occasion Nara was on my shoulder while Fuss the catbird was on my knee enjoying the shelled seeds I offered. Nara, as was her habit when she wished a seed, gave my ear lobe a gentle nip, and, obeying her signal, I proffered an unhulled seed which she accepted, then dropped unopened. Thinking I had given her a hollow seed I offered another which she also dropped. I then offered a third which she refused. As I hulled another for Fuss he left my knee, so I handed it to Nara and she accepted it. From that day until the day of her death (in a later year) she refused, while on my shoulder, to take from me an unopened seed, but never refused a kernel. If I was not with the birds, she hulled these seeds in the normal manner of her kind.

When Sherr, Rée-e and their mates gained their liberty through solving the problem of obstructed exit they gained it under difficult and novel conditions: through intelligent action. Such solving of a problem is brushed aside by some ornithologists as simply "trial and error" or "conditioned reflex": of no significance so far as intelligence is concerned. What does trial and error imply? Can instinct or mechanical reflex, under any definition, explain the working out of basic principles? A problem is presented. A trial is made. The trial fails

160

to resolve it: shows an error. Another trial of a different kind is made and the process of trial continued until the problem either is solved or found, by the individual making the attempt, unsolvable. What constitutes the recognition that the trial of another kind is needed? Is it automatic reaction? There must be thought. The brain lacking in the power of thought—the brain of the idiot—cannot use trial and error. Deliberation is essential.

What did Sherr do? First he tried the obvious. The exit platform was in full view through a mesh almost large enough to allow his body to reach the platform. The mesh being not large enough, he failed. There were many meshes and many were tried, in vain. From time to time he left the covering cage and flew to a branch from which he gazed at the exit. He could see a space underneath and between the cage and platform. He flew down, under and up through this space. When he returned from the trees the cage prevented his flying up from the platform to the nest. Without hesitation he flew down and then up. Not once was he puzzled. He had worked out the pattern and it had remained as a memory. His mature mate, with somewhat slower perception, also solved it, while their immature progeny were unable to do so even to the time of their independence. The implication seems clear and definite.

I have intimated that I have put the cardinal rather far down on the list so far as the intelligence of songbirds goes. Now I wonder. Some time ago, in the middle of winter, a female cardinal was brought to me from the city. A postman delivering the mail almost stepped on this female as he was crossing a lawn. He picked her up and, with that real thoughtfulness of some people, took her at once to a nearby house where he knew there was one who fed and enjoyed the winter birds. Immediately she was brought to me. I found that her right eye was very badly damaged, but she seemed unhurt in any other way.

When I took her in my hand she screamed and bit my fingers viciously—and how these birds can bite! But I succeeded in placing a drop of Argerol in the damaged eye, then placed her in a cage. At once she bumped into the bars and a low roost. She did not fly against the sides of the cage as one would expect a wild bird to do, and I wondered. I shone a flashlight in her normal-looking eye, then passed my hand before it. She did not see. She was totally blind. The optic nerve had been damaged even though the eye itself had not. Should I try to save the injured eye in the hope that the optic nerve would eventually become normal or should I put her to sleep? Sometimes an injured nerve does regain its normal function. Perhaps hers would.

161

Rose-breasted grosbeak Sherree is ready to build her nest

I took out the roost so that she would not further injure her eye when I had to take her into my hand. Like most other birds, she objected strenuously to being caught in the hand and I had to be exceedingly gentle in taking hold of her. Now, not only had I to treat the injured eye, but also to feed her. This was no easy task for I had to pry open her bill and get the food well into the back of her mouth so that she would swallow it. For a week I fed her, but on the second day she neither screamed nor bit when I picked her up, although she did struggle in my hand. And during the second day I did not have to force her bill open. I spoke gently to her, touched her bill with the glass feeder—and—she opened her bill to accept the food.

Each day I wondered more and more as to whether I was right in placing these birds somewhat lower than most other kinds. For before the first week was over, although she still struggled in my hand when I picked her up, and as long as I held her—until I began to wipe away

162

the milky substance in her eye and later the watery exudate—she would remain quietly with her head on one side, with never a move until I had finished my treatment. I had to touch, and draw down, the swollen eyelid so that I might get penicillin ointment well under the lids. I must have hurt her, for that badly swollen eye would have been very painful.

Why did this little bird, one of our wildest and most distrustful, remain so quietly in my hand only when I was treating her injured eye? To touch her eye could not have been soothing to her. Why did she learn so very soon not to scream or bite when I picked her up? Could it be that this bird brain, small though it is, has power to understand?

How different was an eastern kingbird when brought to me! She had a broken wing. She was brought to me too late—the ends of the broken bones had calloused and for that reason would not grow together. Her wing will always droop so badly that to release her would mean quick death by some predator.

She is a flycatcher and therefore almost all of her food is caught on the wing. Even the few berries flycatchers eat are taken off while in flight. When they bathe they fly from a perch and strike the water with a splash and then up to a perch again. This kingbird, also, had to be fed by hand. But it took me twenty days, every half hour during daylight hours, of this hand-feeding before she learned to take food from a dish. When she learned I placed her in the winter quarters with a hundred other birds, none in cages. There she learned at once where the food dishes were and also the water fountain. Yet she, not one of a trustful family in the wild, now comes to my hand for insects I give to her, or she catches them on the wing as I toss. In time I believe she will become as trustful as most of the birds I have. The cardinal never will. Why? We do not know.

And there was the green heron (mentioned earlier), so covered with oil that it could neither fly nor walk, whose fear caused him to jab viciously at the hand that sought to feed him. But he very quickly lost his fear, took my fingers gently in his mandibles, learned to hold his bill open so that water could be poured into it.

These are only a few examples of wide variation or free choice in conduct. Do they not show there is no rigid pattern where there is instinct? That "It's only a bird" can come only from those who do not think, do not know or do not care? Yet, if they cared to know, cared about themselves and others, cared to know the disastrous results were we to have no birds—the expression, "Oh, it's only a bird," would never be heard again.

An Oriole Nest

So still is the air that not a leaf stirs. So still that I can hear clearly the distance-softened flute-like notes of the wood thrush from far back in the swampy edge of the woods. The western sky is black with rolling, turbulent banks of clouds. Sharp jagged strokes of lightning and the distant roll of thunder forewarn of the coming storm. The Baltimore oriole's nest, high up in the willow, begins to sway in a sighing breeze: a forerunner of what can be expected from that distant roar of wind in the tree-tops.

The nest begins to sway in ten-foot arcs as wind and rain lash the willow.

The storm has passed. The nest is still there. But—I seem to see a difference!

This young oriole has built a peculiar nest, far different from any I have seen or heard of before. I have watched her taking the first silvery strands of the inner bark of the flowering dogbane high up to a swaying ten-foot slender drooping branch of the Niobe weeping willow. Instead of weaving the typical pendant bag, she started building a narrow tube, sewing and tying and weaving until it was almost two feet long. Most of the time she worked on the inside of this queer-looking part of an oriole's nest. After she had partly completed it she began building the typical bag on the lower end and reinforcing the tube.

Two weeks after the storm I can see that the tube has lengthened. During these weeks two strong winds have whipped the willow branches. This is a nest that must be watched. If the storm and winds have lengthened the tube, more heavy winds may weaken it still more and allow the nest to fall.

The parents are now entering the nest with food. The eggs have

164

hatched. Occasional high winds again whip their nest so violently that often I wonder how the parents can enter. I wonder how long that tube will stand the strain, for I can see that it is getting longer. Gradually, from day to day, it lengthens until it is nearly three feet long. From the ground, I can see light through it in several places. Occasionally I can see one or two little heads peeking out of the entrance of the nest. Unlike most oriole nests, this one has the entrance hole in the side, close to the top where it joins the tube.

Afraid that another high wind will bring the nest and nestlings to the ground, I borrow a fifteen-foot apple-picking stepladder. To this, with the help of visitors, I attach my extension ladder. Both, some ten feet from the willow, are roped to the trunk. When I climb to the top I find that the tube is so weakened that the nest is in imminent danger of becoming detached. Taking up string, I try to bind the nest to the slender branches on which it is built. I have to hang onto the ladder with one hand for it is so high that, even roped and two visitors holding it, I dare not risk using both hands.

Several days later I examine the nest and find that it is so badly damaged that the young birds could drop out during a heavy wind. I shape a bag of faded cheesecloth as close to the pattern of an oriole nest as I can. I then take down the nest despite the anguished protests of the parents, place the nestlings on the ground, take out the lining

A cheesecloth reinforcement for the oriole nest

and put it in the cheesecloth nest, and then put the little ones inside. I tie this man-made nest as nearly as possible in its original position. The parents accept their new home without much hesitation and, in time, coax their little ones out to that freedom that is a bird's.

The Niobe weeping willow is quiet now. The oriole nest is empty. Above, at the very top of the tree, I hear and sometimes see the last of the little orioles to leave the nest—the youngest. A short distance away I hear the location notes of its brothers and sisters who, one by one, the oldest first, have left the hanging cheesecloth nest. A little sadness creeps in as I watch them go—and gladness: gladness that I have saved five little lives.

Although it is generally thought that one-year-old birds always build perfect nests, I have found this not always so. This Baltimore oriole reminds me of Lady, my blue jay, who built a poor nest on her first attempt, a fairly good one on her second, and a perfect one on her third. My inference is that this oriole was also in her first year; that when she started the tube the inherent something—call it instinct or what you will—that guides a bird in building, was not well developed. That could account, in part, for the number of young orioles that have been picked up and brought to me through the years. It might also, in some measure, account for the large number of other species that are brought for my care.

A male Baltimore oriole feeding one of his nestlings,
just out of the nest but still unable to fly

A Plea

So many are brought to me: tiny, naked nestlings taken from thought-less boys who have robbed the parents of their little ones; feathered youngsters taken from a prowling cat; some picked off the ground where they had fallen when hunger pangs forced them to climb from the nest a day or two too soon, both parents killed in some unknown way. And older birds: birds with broken wings—cars travel fast these days—concussions from striking picture windows they could not see. You know, I thought two hundred and fifty in a year were so many; yet, how few they were when I think of that wonderful woman in Seattle, Della Schumaker, who has five to six hundred brought to her each year. Is she ever able to rest or sleep? Yes, a little. She gets an average of about two hours sleep a night when the deluge comes.

Try, with us, to protect our disappearing songbirds. Believe it or not, you and I cannot live without them. Without them insects *can* take over, despite the deadly biocides (the insecticides that are becoming more deadly every year as injurious insects become resistant to each one in turn), the so-called pesticides that are taking the lives of countless millions of our songbirds—songbirds that are so necessary if we are to live—*every year*. If we should ever allow them to die out—a great continental desert!

What can *you* do about these sometime-orphans or little ones that have fallen from the nest? Unfortunately, few know how or what to feed an unfledged or callow nestling. On the lawn, in the garden, beside a country road, particularly in or near a town or village, you hear a chirping note, probably an unfamiliar note, and there, a few feet away, a chunky, tailless little bird with heavily spotted breast. A little lost bird! You pick it up, take it into the house and put into that wide-open, coaxing mouth—what? Perhaps some dry bread, perhaps some ice-cold raw beef right out of the refrigerator—or perhaps even some canary seed. And the little robin dies.

Don't pick a young bird up unless you find it where a cat can get it. (Then, put it on a branch high out of reach of one of the worst of all enemies of little birds.) Watch it for a while. In nine cases out of ten the parents know where it is. You heard that single note, perhaps the loud chirp of a young robin, perhaps the tiny chirp of some small species. That is what we call the "location" note. After the young birds have left the nest their own distinctive location note is uttered at short intervals all day long. This is so the parents will know always just where the youngster is. If, after an hour or more, you do not see the one you have been watching being fed, you will know that very likely something has happened to the parents. Then, take it in. It needs your help and care—to live.

If the baby bird is bare of feathers or with few—it will be rare to find one so naked on the ground—it will need to be kept very warm until the feathers cover well the whole small body. The reason for this is that the parent's brood spot has a temperature of about 105 degrees and she broods them often so that they will not become chilled. Wrap the little one in a piece of woollen cloth and place this close to an electric light bulb—not so close that there will be any chance of burning— or on top of a hot water bottle. But remember to put two or three layers of cloth between the bird and the bottle. Keep the little bird warm—about ninety degrees—until it is well feathered. Should it already be feathered, as most of them are when you find them, it will not need heat.

Blue jay youngsters

If "fear" has not developed, when you go near it will open wide that beautiful pink or orange mouth. It will take any food you give it, readily. As soon as possible make what we call a steamed custard. This is simply *only* the contents of an egg beaten up in one cup of milk and put on top of the teakettle until well cooked. (Should the young one be only partly feathered, use only the yolk of egg until feathers are well grown.) Mix equal parts of custard and pablum or some other similar baby food sufficient for one day. Keep this at room temperature. Fresh custard should be made every second day.

For highly insectivorous birds such as swallows, nighthawks, flycatchers and others—birds that live entirely or almost entirely on insects—a different rearing food must be used. In fact, this different rearing food is exceptionally good for all young songbirds.

Mix well together the following:

1 $3\frac{1}{2}$-ounce tin strained beef heart
2 tablespoons mashed potatoes (not salted)
1 tablespoon mashed or finely grated carrots
2 tablespoons butter
1 teaspoon honey (not entirely necessary)
4 drops Vi-Penta or other concentrated vitamins

Keep in refrigerator but be sure to feed at room temperature.

A feeding stick may be made of a small branch—elderberry makes the best food stick. Make a slanting cut on one end of the wood and scoop out the pith. Round the end and make it smooth with a nail sander. If you cannot secure a cane with pith inside, carefully make the slanted end spoon-like so as to hold a small quantity of food. A food stick a little larger than a lead pencil is about right for a bird the size of a robin. Use a smaller or larger stick according to the size of the bird.

Feed small amounts at a time. If the little bird is very young (and it will be, more or less, if it gapes), you will need to feed it a little— several helpings—every fifteen minutes. You will be surprised at the amount it can eat. As it grows older you may feed it until its crop is full—you can see the lower part of the neck swell with food—once every half hour. At all ages give the young one a few drops of water occasionally, using a medicine dropper: just one drop at a time. This feeding must be kept up until it is a month old, or when it begins to notice the food in the cup and starts feeding itself. You can judge of the age fairly well by the length of the tail. At eight to nine days the tail feathers of many species will be about an eighth of an inch long.

It will be well to keep the youngster a week or so after it has begun to feed itself. Then, if it is well and strong, you must release it. Let it go where you know others of its kind are in the vicinity. Better, if possible (except for robins and house sparrows, which become wild quickly), as far away from human beings as you can so that it may regain its fear of them.

Should you have to pick up and care for a young bird in which fear has developed, you can have a difficult time for a day or two. This bird will not gape for food. It must be force-fed until it will gape. Hold the youngster in your left hand with forefinger and thumb around its neck. Dip up a small amount of food on the food stick and holding the stick between your right thumb and forefinger, pry open the bill with the nail of your little finger and hold the bill open with the tips of thumb and forefinger of your left hand. Then insert the food beyond the fork of the tongue. See that it swallows the food before repeating. Give several small helpings each time before putting it back in its cage or box. Some will learn what is expected in a short time; others may take as many as three days.

If there has been some injury that prevents flying well, then it would be wise not to release it. Either take it to a zoo—most have facilities for keeping birds—or keep it yourself. If the latter—it is rarely wise to cage our native birds—do not put it in a small canary or budgie cage. Make as large a one as possible—give it plenty of flying room.

Boys: it is you in particular that I wish to talk to about birds and all the other little wild creatures we have, or should have, about us. I wish to show you not only that we cannot live without birds but that we must depend upon you so that we shall not be without them. As the late Julia Kenley wrote in one of her many books on nature:

... let us see what would happen if nature were suddenly to do away with all the bird people. What would that mean—? A horrible calamity! The insects of the world, laying their eggs by the billion every second, every minute of the day, would increase at such a rate, now there were no birds to eat them, that in a very little time the earth would be nothing more than a great, bleak, dusty desert! Year by year her green fur of trees and grass would be eaten to the bone. The sky would be bare, not a white sail of cloud to bring us a cargo of rain! A hot deserted planet, a great ball of bugs, battling with other bugs as to which would be the first to be devoured!
It would seem then, that the birds play a much more practical part in the life of the earth than does man himself. Nature put the birds here, and one of their most important uses is to keep down the myriad of insect pests, as well as policing the small animals on which the owls and hawks feed.... nature's plan would always work well for them if it were not for cats and shotguns, for the little-boy thieves of eggs and nests, and for the *ignorance* and *indifference* [my italics] of nine people out of ten as to what a bird really means.

170

I am telling you this because during the last ten years or so a bird's chances of living, and helping *us* to live, diminished almost unbelievably. In the past probably the greatest danger to bird-life was the domestic cat. For in the United States alone, where most of our birds winter, it has been estimated by those who should know that over one hundred million birds are killed by cats each year. That is a lot of birds.

Some seventy-five years ago I saw the western prairies alive with birds: the sloughs a paradise for terns and waders; the wild geese, ducks and cranes in unbelievable numbers. Where are these great numbers today? Twenty-five years ago, my sanctuary, the surrounding meadow and woods, were also alive with birds. Where today are the ovenbird, red-eyed vireo, veery, scarlet tanager; bluebird; mourning and yellow-throated warblers and the ruffed grouse?

Now there are other terrible dangers for the birds. There are tens of thousands of picture windows on the continent and millions of birds are killed on those each year. There are over eight thousand TV and radio towers on this continent. Many are located on migration routes. The morning after a heavy fall migration of birds it was estimated that within a one-mile radius of a TV tower in Wisconsin there were twenty thousand dead birds of some seventy-five species.

And, of course, enormous numbers are killed on the highways by cars every year. On top of all this there are now the deadly insect sprays which are killing, probably, hundreds of millions of birds each year. I know, for example, of three lawns sprayed to kill white grubs where forty-nine dead robins and a number of other birds were picked up.

Are we to continue this great slaughter? Shall I, shortly, have to pass on to someone who may wish to carry on my studies—a "sanctuary" in name only?